KU-670-207

WILD GYM
50 WAYS TO GET FIT OUTDOORS

Warwickshire College
00109438

First published in 2008 by
Guardian Books, 119 Farringdon Road, London EC1R 3ER
guardianbooks.co.uk

Guardian Books is an imprint of Guardian News and Media Ltd.

10 9 8 7 6 5 4 3 2 1

A CIP record for this book is available from the British Library.

ISBN: 978-0-85265-094-3

Design: Two Associates

Printed and bound in Germany by Mohn Media

WILD GYM

50 WAYS TO GET FIT OUTDOORS

PETA BEE

gb

CONTENTS

Image courtesy of the Countryside Alliance

WILD GYM INTRODUCTION

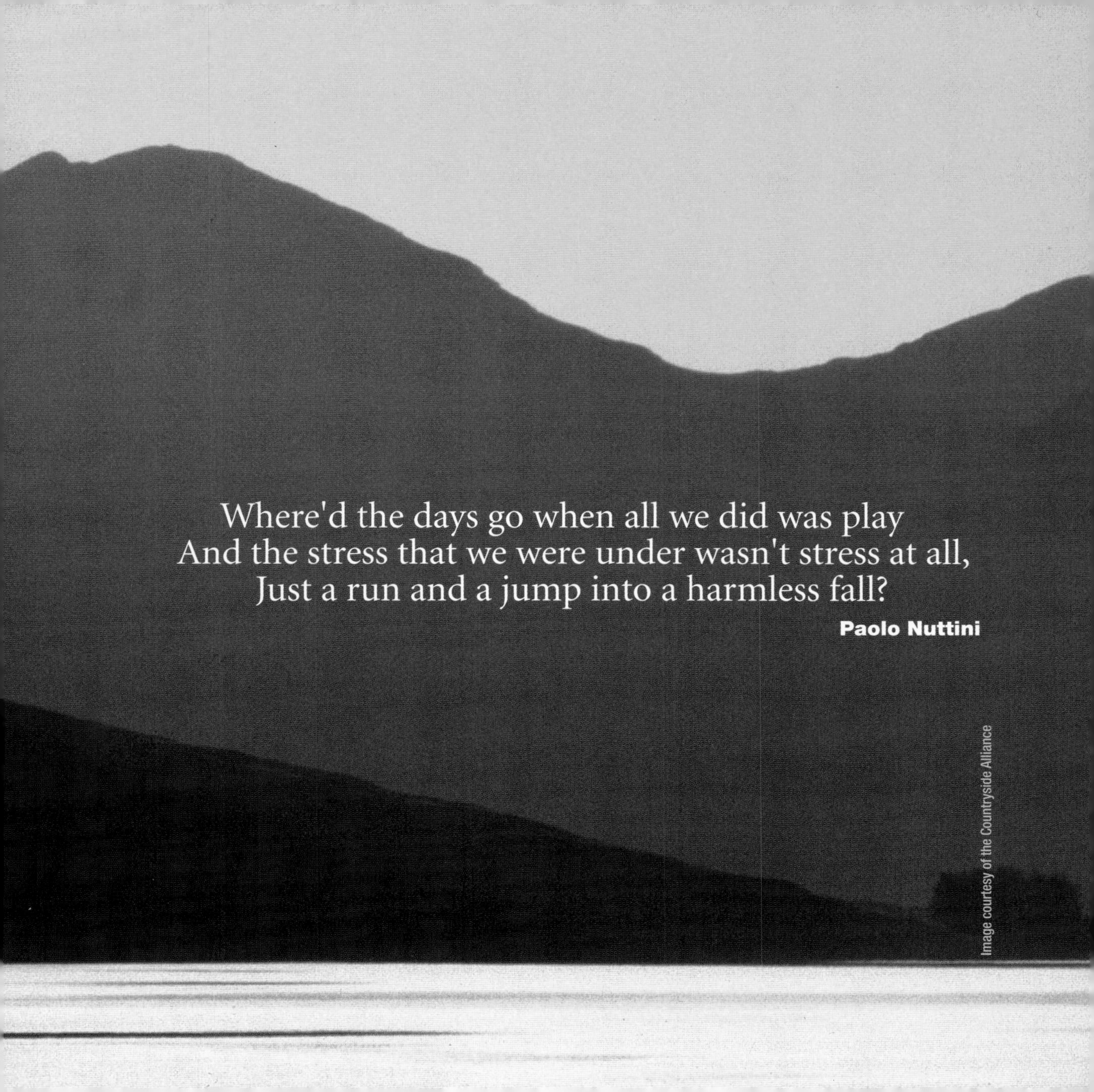
Where'd the days go when all we did was play
And the stress that we were under wasn't stress at all,
Just a run and a jump into a harmless fall?
Paolo Nuttini

Image courtesy of the Countryside Alliance

WHAT HAPPENED TO OUR LOVE AFFAIR WITH NATURE and being outside? 100 years ago, the average Briton spent a large percentage of their waking hours outdoors. They walked or cycled to work, were more likely to have jobs involving exposure to the elements and their physical activity was conducted almost exclusively in the wind, sun, snow or rain. Today, inhabitants of the industrialised west spend 93 per cent of their time inside the confines of four walls, largely disconnected from nature and the environment. Britons work the longest hours in Europe – up to 60 hours a week – which, for a lot of people, means that most daylight hours are spent desk-bound after arriving in a centrally-heated or air-conditioned car, train or bus.

Children, too, lead increasingly closeted lives. From the earliest age they spend most of their time inside – watching television, playing video games and hunched over a computer. A study by the UK charity, The Children's Society, revealed that many parents deny their children the chance to enjoy the freedom they had as youngsters because of fears for their safety. Almost half of the adults questioned believed children should not be allowed out alone or with friends until they were 14. Another report by the Royal Society for the Prevention of Accidents suggested that today's children are more likely to suffer injuries brought on by playing computer games than from climbing a tree or jumping a ditch. The relationship between kids and their bikes is especially telling – in 1995, 68 per cent of children ages seven to 11 rode a bike at least six times a year – now surveys suggest that fewer than half do the same. Inactive children are more likely to become inactive adults, and in a society facing the economic and social repercussions of soaring obesity statistics, these findings are especially worrying.

Image courtesy of the Countryside Alliance

Both images courtesy of sportengland.org/promotingsport

The benefits of getting outside are as significant for those in their 70s and older as they are for the very young. Many researchers have found that regular exercise can slow or even reverse some of the effects of aging that were once thought to be inevitable. When a group of 64 volunteers with an average age of 84 were asked to exercise by walking or resistance training or do nothing, those who walked showed significant improvements in their health. After 16 weeks they had lower blood pressure, improved body strength, better flexibility and higher scores in tests of balance and coordination when compared with the non-exercisers. In the very old, the physically active are far less likely to develop problems walking or climbing stairs. There are confirmed advantages too for blood pressure, bone density and self-esteem that come with lifelong exercise. Aerobic activity, in particular, has been shown to prevent age-related mental decline – researchers reported that exercise inhibits Alzheimer-like symptoms in mice and could do the same in humans.

* Regular exercise can slow or even reverse some of the effects of ageing that were thought to be inevitable

THE BIOPHILIA HYPOTHESIS

For many people, it is not unusual for 24 hours to pass without the wind on their face or the sun on their backs. We socialise and shop indoors – in bars, restaurants or at home, and one in seven people exercises indoors at gyms, health-clubs or swimming pools. While this shift in modern lifestyles is undoubtedly setting the current generation of children and adults up for a more rotund existence than their predecessors, there are deeper issues at play. Human beings were not designed to behave this way. In evolutionary terms, our growing disconnection with nature has occurred quite rapidly, mirroring the growth and sprawl of urban conurbations. Many experts believe the increasing amount of time spent indoors is responsible for a corresponding rise in mental health problems; one in every four GP consultations is for depression, anxiety, stress or other more severe mental health conditions.

Scientists have proven that humans have an innate attraction to nature called biophilia – and that reverting back to our ancestors' habits of being outside more often can boost mental health. Research from Japan and the Netherlands has shown that just living close to green space means people live longer and enjoy better health; even a view of the great outdoors can do wonders for the mood. In one groundbreaking experiment, it was shown how patients recovering from identical operations were more likely to get better quicker, have fewer side effects and need fewer painkillers if they had a view of nature from their hospital beds rather than a brick wall. However, it is widely agreed that the synergistic effects of physical activity combined with an outdoor environment that have the most potent effects on wellbeing. The Mental Health Foundation says outdoor exercise provides a sense of accomplishment participants might not get at the gym. Likewise, a report by the Countryside Recreation Network (CRN) found that self-esteem was significantly boosted and weight lost in nine out of ten people who switched from exercising indoors to out.

Both images courtesy of the Countryside Alliance

DAYLIGHT DEFICIENCY

Thanks to sedentary lifestyles and sun damage warnings, most Britons receive too little vitamin D. Few foods contain it naturally (although egg yolks, oily fish and fortified margarine and cereal are good sources) – the main provider is the sun since the vitamin is synthesised when chemicals in the skin react to ultraviolet rays. A lack of exposure to natural daylight could put you at risk of chronic conditions such as heart disease.

Getting enough vitamin D should be easy. Between 80 and 100 per cent of our requirement of it is met by sunlight, and just 30 minutes of exposure to the face and arms each day between April and October, when the sun's rays are strongest, is enough to ensure adequate levels for the rest of the year (in Britain almost no vitamin D is generated in the skin in winter because the solar radiation contains too little ultraviolet light). There is currently no official daily dietary recommendation for vitamin D in the UK, but the Institute of Food Research in Norwich says that if the US adequate intake of five micrograms (mg) were applied here, 90 per cent of the population would fall short. A study at Harvard University revealed that an adequate vitamin D intake can reduce the risk of all types of cancer by up to 30 per cent. Insufficient levels have also been linked to other conditions, including multiple sclerosis, heart disease and calcification of the arteries, while higher levels of vitamin D reduces inflammation in blood vessels.

Image courtesy of the Countryside Alliance

THERE ARE COUNTLESS OTHER PHYSICAL BENEFITS OF HEADING OUTSIDE. Researchers at the American Academy of Dermatology, for example, found that skin problems, ranging from acne to blisters, are much higher among people who work indoors and Allergy UK claims that the humidity caused by heating and a lack of ventilation creates the ideal environment for mould, dust mites and other allergens to thrive, meaning asthma, eczema and hayfever are a much higher risk.

Trawl through scientific literature and there are literally hundreds of papers confirming that outdoors is better than indoors when it comes to being active. And the beauty of a wild gym is that it can be anything you want or anywhere you happen to be at the time. It might constitute the most extreme challenges or consist of a form of comfort-activity, something you know is going to leave you with a glow of accomplishment when it is done. What matters is the vastness of the sky above you and the sense of freedom that comes with embracing your surroundings.

Image courtesy of Plas y Brenin, pyb.co.uk

HOW OUTDOOR EXERCISE WENT INDOORS

Gyms. You join, you pay, but do you turn up? Statistically, the answer is of course you don't. Surveys by the fitness industry show that most people throw in the towel six months after forking out a hefty gym subscription. For anyone who has ever found themselves in this position (including me), it's not hard to see why.

For every plus point of gyms, there is a nagging negative that leaves you questioning whether this is what exercise is really all about. Part of the reason so many of us succumb to their lure is through a sense of guilt and obligation. There is immense societal pressure to be fitter and healthier and a monthly direct debit to a gym goes a little way to easing the conscience. Yet even among those who do claim to attend regularly, one fifth actually go to their health club once a month or less often. They would burn far more calories, stave off ill-health and boost their spirit to a greater extent with a brisk daily walk.

In reality, time never passes so slowly as it does in a gym. Members plug into their headphones or enter a solitary zone of silence as they plod on their treadmill or pedal their bike. Eye contact is rarely made; communication is minimal. Three quarters of gym members even schedule their visits to coincide with a specific television programme. Researchers found that many gym members become so engrossed in a TV show that they simply go through the motions of exercise – slowly pedalling on a bike, stepping on a stairclimber or inching along on the treadmill – and barely breaking sweat.

In fact, the gyms themselves gobble up energy at a far faster rate than their members expend it. With their heated pools and saunas, air conditioning and central heating systems, bright lighting, laundry demands and, of course, high tech exercise machines, many of which need some form of powering, they are far from green in the ethical sense. Some gym owners have jumped onto the renewable energy treadmill – the California Fitness Club in Hong Kong, for instance, is among the first to wire up gym machines to the building's lighting system. In much the same way as the dynamo lights on bicycles, the idea is that the harder and longer you pedal, the more energy is harnessed to generate electrical power. A human can generate roughly 125 watts – one-sixth horsepower – of continuous power by pedalling. But these forward thinking fitness industry moguls are surely missing

* Surveys by the fitness industry show that most people throw in the towel six months after forking out a hefty gym subscription

Photograph by Martin Argles

the point. Were exercise performed outdoors in a natural environment, there would be no need to transfer human power into a reuseable source because you wouldn't need to power 17 treadmills, 35 televisions and a vibrating platform in the first place.

In short, gyms are to fitness what convenience food is to the diet. Of course they have a place in society and fulfil the needs of many. They are accessible, if a little expensive, and appeal to those who are hoping for instant results. Wild gyms take a little more effort, a little more planning and a little more dedication. They are pure and unadulterated – an organic form of fitness that will supply pleasure and pleasing results on the scales in bucket-loads.

SIX UNLIKELY HEALTH HAZARDS OF THE GYM

You may think a gym is a healthier option than heading outdoors into a world of pollution, darkness and traffic, but they can harbour hazards of their own:

1 Hot tubs: poorly-maintained hot-tubs can be a breeding ground for potentially dangerous bacteria. Whereas a teaspoon of tap water contains about 138 bacteria, a teaspoon of whirlpool tub water had an average of 2.17 million bugs in one American study. Bacteria derived from faeces were present in 95 per cent of samples, while 34 per cent contained potentially deadly staphylococcus bacteria.

2 Indoor pools: Outbreaks of cryptosporidium, a nasty stomach complaint, are sometimes linked to swimming pools. Often, it is caused by swallowing contaminated water. Ironically, chemicals such as chlorine which are added to pools to kill off potentially harmful bacteria can also be problematic. One survey tested water from eight pools in the London area and found levels of chemical by-products, called trihalomethanes were much higher in pool water than in tap water.

Photograph by Don McPhee

3 Saunas and steam rooms: Saunas have been found to contain high levels of citrobacter freundii bacteria, an agent of infections including pneumonia, blood and urinary tract infections in one UK survey. Wooden benches in saunas and steam rooms have lots of crevices, providing ideal gaps for bacteria to colonise.

Image courtesy of sportengland.org/promotingsport.

4 Gym equipment: Researchers found high amounts of staphylococcus epidermis, which causes skin infections, on the bench-press headrests and dumbbells in UK gyms. Boxing gloves contained a micrococcus species of bacteria that can occasionally cause infections, and the sweaty residue on gym equipment used in quick succession, such as weights and exercise bikes, could also harbour streptococcal infections and even candida, the germ that causes yeast infection.

5 Air conditioning: It might seem a blessing when the weather is sweltering, but air conditioning in gyms may contribute to infection with a range of viruses. The lining of the nose is covered with a thin layer of mucus, which protects against infection. Since air conditioners extract moisture from the air, they may cause some drying of the protective mucus blanket in the nose and predispose us to infection. The cold air may also help viruses to establish a hold, as they reproduce better in a cold nose.

6 Noise pollution: Gyms are getting noisier according to research by the Royal National Institute for the Deaf (RNID). Regular exposure to noise levels above 85 decibels has been shown to increase the risk of tinnitus (ringing in the ears) and of deafness. According to the RNID, aerobics classes regularly exceed 90dB. A noisy environment has even been linked to heart disease by a team of German cardiologists from the Charité University Medical Centre in Berlin. Women who regularly spent time in a generally noisy environment were three times more likely to have a heart attack.

SO WHAT'S YOUR EXCUSE?

It is easy to think of reasons not to exercise and easier still to come up with excuses not to go outside when it is cold, dark and you live in a city. But are those excuses viable?

1 **Too dark:** Come winter, it may be dark when you get up and when you get home, but that shouldn't stop you heading outside. Following simple safety advice will enable you to explore your wild gym even in the dark. If you go for a run, walk or cycle, leave a note at home stating when you left, where you'll be running and when you expect to return, keeping to populated and well-lit areas, and never sticking to exactly the same route. Wear reflective clothing and always carry some form of identification.

2 **Too hot:** During the summer months, timing is key to making sure you can exercise outside safely. It is unwise to go for a run or cycle at the hottest time of the day (midday to early afternoon) and far preferable to go in the morning or early evening. If the weather is warm when you head out, make sure you take sensible precautions: wear loose, lightweight clothing, a peaked cap to shield your eyes and head from the intense sun and always apply sweat-resistant sunscreen – many sports people don't and the risk of skin cancer in this group is higher as a result. Staying well hydrated is also vital – in hot weather it is advisable to drink around one litre of water or sports drinks for every hour of exercise. Drink more than that and you risk hyponatraemia, or water intoxication, a condition in which sodium levels and other body salts, or electrolytes, in the blood become dangerously diluted.

3 **Too cold:** Rather than being an excuse to snuggle up in front of the fire, researchers have found that we benefit more from exercising outdoors when temperatures begin to drop. Exercising in hot weather is harder – activity causes the body to generate more heat and you have to get rid of this through the evaporation of sweat. It is, in fact, much easier to exercise in the cold as your body is better able to tolerate activity which means you can

keep going for longer. Even better news is the fact that fat-burning is boosted by cold weather. When a frosty gust strikes your skin, it prompts the brain to spur the adrenal glands into action. They release surplus amounts of a key hormone called epinephrine (or adrenaline) that forces the fat cells to push increased amounts of fat into the blood. The fat is then metabolised at a faster rate by the muscles. There are, of course, a few precautions that need to be taken during a cold snap. Because it takes longer for muscles to warm up, you will need to progress more slowly into your activity otherwise you risk damaging ill-prepared muscles and tendons. And there is no truth in the myth that exercising in cold weather freezes the lungs – the human body is amazing in its ability to humidify air.

Image courtesy of Plas y Brenin, pyb.co.uk

4 Too dangerous: Safety among exercisers, especially for women who live in urban areas has received an undeserved bad press. Official crime figures show that attacks on women outside the home are relatively infrequent; young men, in fact, are more often the victims of assault. There are a few sensible precautions you should take: carry a mobile phone or enough change to make a call or get the bus or taxi home if you are walking or running alone and try to do several shorter routes past your house rather than one long run or cycle. Don't use headphones outdoors – not only will you not be able to hear cars or cyclists but also someone approaching who intends to do you harm. Bear in mind, too, that the most common form of attack on joggers and walkers is not by muggers but by dogs.

5 Too urban: A common misconception is that outdoor exercise is best suited to the countryside: far from it. For some people the urban jungle is far superior. For years I was a confirmed city dweller and while I frequently got an overwhelming urge to make a bolt for greenery and fresh air at weekends, I was never at a loss to find somewhere equally inspiring and tranquil in which to create a wild gym well within the green belt. Indeed, now that I live in the middle of some of England's most beautiful rolling countryside with woods, a river and miles of open space on my doorstep, I sometimes crave concrete and the anonymity of city-strolling in which you can lose yourself in spite of being surrounded by crowds and traffic.

Cities offer just as much scope for outdoor exercise as anywhere else. In England alone, there are 188,700 km of public footpaths and rights of way, and they are not just in far-flung rural corners of the country. Three quarters of people in Britain – no matter where their home – also live within two miles of a National Cycle Network route. Neither are towns and cities necessarily the most risky places when it comes to pollution. While they do sometimes exceed government standards for levels of

Left: Courtesy of sportengland.org/promotingsport Right: Photograph by Don McPhee

nitrogen dioxide in the air, the most damaging for outdoor exercisers is a high ozone level, which is more usually found in rural areas. Dartmoor, the Suffolk coast and parts of the Peak District regularly exceed the highest ozone levels in the UK.

Furthermore, most people assume that pollution only occurs outdoors – it does not cross their mind that indoor pollution is potentially as hazardous. Studies by the US Environmental Protection Agency have shown that levels of air pollutants indoors may be anywhere from two to five times greater than outdoors, and in some cases more than 100 times greater– the quality of air breathed in while sitting in a car is 18 times worse than it is outside.

6 Too time-crunched: If long working hours and high levels of stress are uppermost on your list of reasons for not exercising, then your abstinence is certainly counter-productive. It has long been known that gentle aerobic exercise, like walking, stimulates the

Photograph by David Sillitoe

production of endorphins – the natural painkillers and mood-enhancers produced in the brain. But there are additional reasons why exercise is such a potent stress-buster. Researchers found that levels of the chemical phenylethylamine, similar in structure to amphetamines, increase substantially during exercise to produce a significant mood-boosting effect. So effective is exercise at lifting the spirits that a report by the Mental Health Foundation (MHF) urged doctors to offer exercise on prescription instead of drugs in the treatment of mild to moderate depression. And the mental health charity, MIND, says ecotherapy – getting outdoors and active in a green environment – is the best way to boost mental wellbeing. In one of its studies, 71 per cent of people who did outdoor activities ranging from kite-flying to walking said it helped boost their mood.

7 Too self-conscious: Most people, when questioned, admit to feeling embarrassed about venturing outside in their workout gear for the first time, regardless of their shape and size. But it has been proven time and again by researchers that the most effective way to boost body image and self-esteem is through exercise. And when that exercise is outdoors, you escape the scrutiny of other gym members and the self-torture of facing yourself in mirrors as you work out. If you do initially dread the thought of outdoor activity, try to stay focused on the task in hand and true to your own sense of purpose. In time, your renewed confidence will override any self-consciousness and you will wonder how you ever even contemplated forking out for a hefty gym subscription.

CHAPTER 1
WILD GYM IN THE CITY

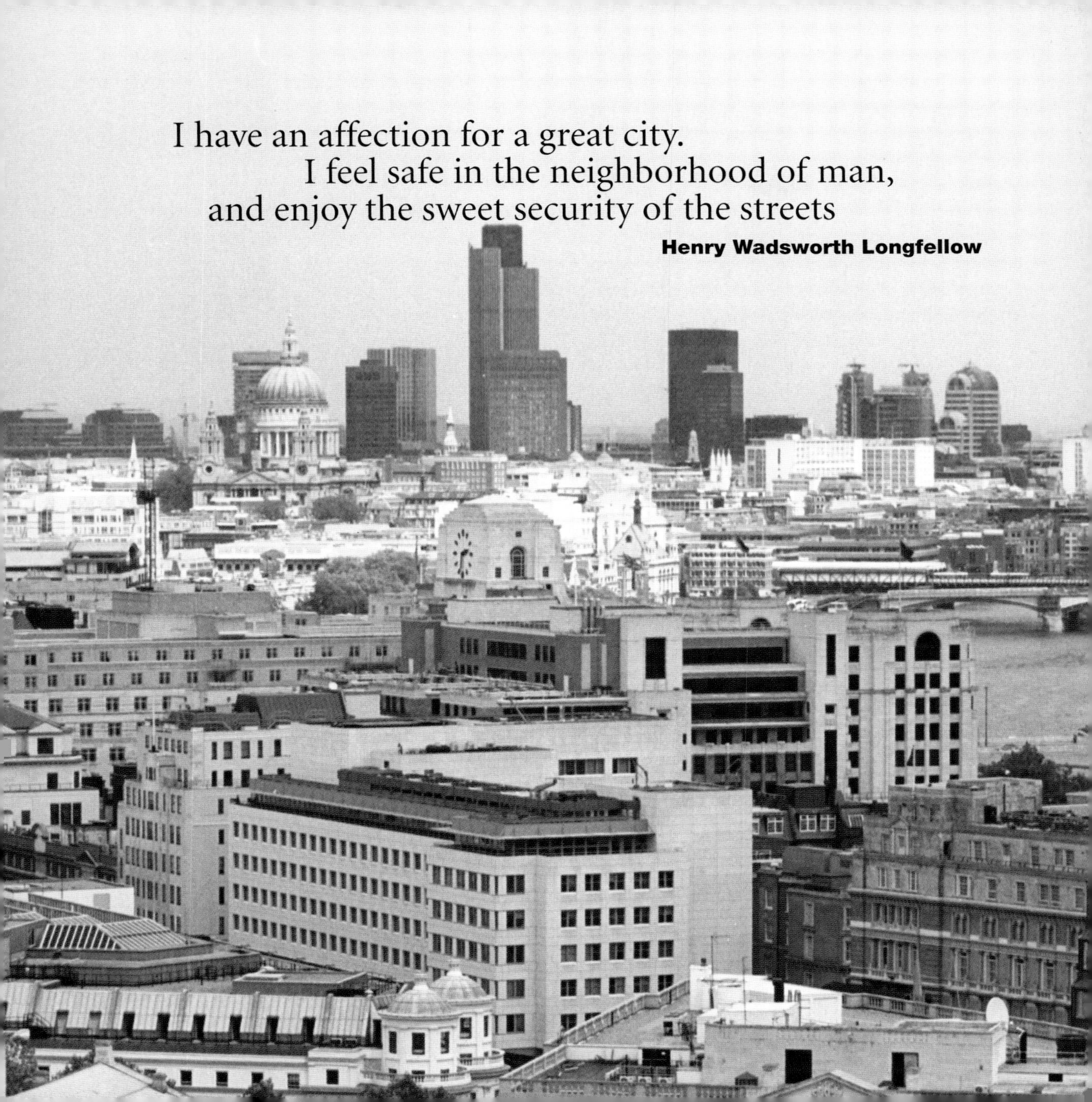
I have an affection for a great city.
I feel safe in the neighborhood of man,
and enjoy the sweet security of the streets
Henry Wadsworth Longfellow

It is often assumed that parks and playing fields squeezed into urban spaces will simply never match what the countryside has to offer when it comes to opportunities for being active. Nothing could be further from the truth. In fact, the good news for the 80 per cent of people in the UK who live in urban areas is that towns and cities have wild gyms entirely of their own. These may be edgier and not always as obvious as those of their rural counterparts but are no less challenging or rewarding.

Studies have discounted the myth that city dwellers are lazy, relying on cars, lifts and escalators to get around. Instead researchers have found that urbanites are more likely to be active just because of where they live. Cities are literally designed to force people to walk and to climb stairs often at top speed, as a combination of public transport and leg power is the primary means of inner-city commuting. Research has shown that people who live in built-up areas tend to walk further than people who live in the country and, due to the pace of life, also to do it faster.

But it is not just the calorie-burning, muscle building and invigorating effects of urban activity that inspire people to do more. Cities can be isolating and lonely until you discover the micro-communities that thrive within them. Embracing a new sport or activity can open your eyes to people, places and a sense of cohesiveness you never knew existed within your own locale, as well as introducing a sense of freedom to what can often be a fairly claustrophobic lifestyle.

People living in towns and cities are also likely to have accessibility to a range of wild gym facilities that rural dwellers might only dream of. Where else but in a town or city would you find outdoor ice rinks, purpose-built climbing walls and floodlit running tracks, all-weather football pitches and outdoor swimming pools and lidos? Increasingly, urban councils are aiming to meet the needs of a wider range of the population too. There are walking, hiking and jogging clubs for the over 60s, athletics, football and cycling clubs for teenagers and more opportunities and provisions for people with a disability than ever before. Dedicated cycling routes in cities allow you to skirt traffic jams, whilst running through parks and along pavements can introduce you to far-flung corners of your local area.

Outdoor exercise in an urban environment provides a sense of tranquility that is altogether different but no less satisfying to the soul than the peace and quiet you get in the countryside. One thing is certain, urban exercise is always going to be unpredictable. All the more reason to make the most of what the city has to offer.

POWER WALKING

It's free, convenient, requires no special skill and can get you from A to B far more quickly than sitting in a traffic jam. Power walking (also called fitness or health walking) is officially the nation's favourite fitness activity with more than half the population claiming to do it at some time according to government surveys. Little wonder when researchers have shown regularly putting your best foot forward will lower the risk of heart disease, cancer, diabetes and, of course, a thickening girth. It can also boost your brainpower and ward off the effects of ageing, studies have found. Unlike competitive racewalking, with its unnatural hip-shift, and Nordic walking (see page 32) there is no official definition and, most refreshingly of all, there are no rules. If you walk at a purposeful pace using good technique, then you can consider yourself a power walker.

HOW TO DO IT

Almost everyone can walk, but a glance down the average high street is enough to reveal that techniques can vary from shuffle to waddle and from sprint to slouch. A good style will enable you to walk efficiently and reduce the risk of injury. Stand up straight with your arms by your sides, making sure your stomach muscles are pulled in. Look about five to six metres ahead and keep your shoulders relaxed. Bend your elbows at a 90-degree angle, but don't clench your fists. As you step forward with your right foot, move your arms in opposition (ie: as your left arm moves forward, your right moves back). Do not over-stride and breathe evenly and regularly as you walk.

EQUIPMENT

■ **Shoes** – For most city walking, a supportive, lightweight, flexible and moderately cushioned pair of trainers will suffice. More demanding terrain and off-road walking will require shoes with a higher cut or boots to provide ankle support.

■ **Pedometer** – A device that counts the number of steps taken and the distance covered is the most useful tool for walkers. They cost very little, but the National Step-O-Meter Programme (NSP) offers NHS patients free use of a pedometer – ask your GP for details. Health experts recommend that walking 10,000 steps (about five miles in total, but this comprises every step you take from walking to the bathroom to shopping) should be the daily aim just to stay healthy. At least 16,000 steps a day is probably required for weight loss.

■ **Hand weights** – As you get fitter, these are a good option to add a resistance element to your walking. A potential downside of power walking is its limited ability to strengthen the upper body. Although pumping the arms will go some way

towards remedying this, adding light hand weights will make sure that the arm, pectoral (chest) and shoulder muscles get a workout too.

BODY BOOSTING

■ **Calories** – Strolling along at 3.5 mph (a 17 minute mile) will burn 2.4 calories an hour for every pound of your body weight (that's 340 calories for someone who weighs ten stone). Increase your speed to 4.5 mph (a 13 minute mile) and you almost double the calories used. As a rough guide, though, about 100 calories are burned for every mile walked.

■ **Muscles** – With each stride you take, you will strengthen and tone the gluteus maximus muscle in your bottom, the iliopsoas muscles at the front of the hips and the hamstrings, quadriceps and calf muscles in the upper and lower legs. As you pump your arms, the bicep and tricep muscles are also recruited.

■ **Bones** – Walking is a weight-bearing exercise and among the most effective bone-building exercises.

OUTDOORS V INDOORS

It is not just the psychological benefits that make it worthwhile for walkers to be outside. Varying gradients and terrain mean that outdoor walking is better by far when it comes to getting you fit. Soft surfaces, such as mud, sand or grass, require more energy than you would use walking on a treadmill; every time your foot hits the ground it creates a small depression so that the leg muscles must work harder to push upwards and forwards for the next step. Even tarmac and concrete, with their unpredictable inclines, twists and turns, should be included for variety.

RISK FACTOR

Low-risk, provided you adhere to usual traffic safety precautions.

COST £

Image courtesy of Walk the Walk breast cancer charity

ALSO TRY

Nordic walking – Cross-country skiers invented the concept of walking with ski poles as a form of summer training, but now it is a fitness method in its own right. Studies have shown that using poles forces people to walk faster without really trying – on average 20 per cent more calories are burned by walkers who carry poles. Researchers also found that poles increase upper body strength by 40 per cent and reduced the strain on hips, ankles and knees by 26 per cent compared with running. Classes are available to teach technique and to introduce you to other pole-walkers.

Image courtesy of Nordic Walking UK

URBAN RUNNING

At the end of the 1980s we were told how slapping pavements with the soles of our feet was no good for our joints and inhaling traffic fumes about as beneficial to our lungs as a pack of cigarettes. Out went the jogging boom and in its place came a trend for 'trail running', hailed as the healthiest way to run, breathing in fresh air while running along country tracks and woodland paths. This presented an obvious problem for the average city dweller, who was more interested in the streets outside their front door than stumbling through mud and over tree-roots many miles away. Fortunately, as a result of more recent research, experts have concluded that pollution and pavements are not nearly so harmful as was once thought, and that the benefits of running – in any environment – far outweigh the risks. So urban running has become trail running's city counterpart – gritty and grimy but no less exhilarating.

Photograph by David Levene

HOW TO DO IT

The best thing about urban running is that it can be done day or night. Since cities can offer well-lit courses and routes, they are great places to run in the evenings, although, for safety reasons, it is a good idea to go in groups. Athletics and running clubs often meet on at least two evenings a week and encourage newcomers to join in. Urban running will involve a fair bit of dodging and side-stepping of obstacles – such as lampposts, kerbs, raised paving stones, traffic and people – so you will need to be extra vigilant while moving at speed. In general, though, the technique is the same as you would use on countryside trails: a rolling heel to ball of the foot action, arms held at right angles with hands almost brushing the hipbones as you pump them backwards and forwards, and head kept facing forward and perfectly still.

EQUIPMENT

Some sports shoe manufacturers have developed specialist urban running shoes with sticky, well-gripped soles for extra traction on slippery pavements. Others have created running shoes that are highly reflective when exposed to street and car lights. While these are useful additions, they are not essential and you can get by with a good pair of road-running trainers.

BODY BOOSTING

■ **Muscles** – Running uses all the major muscles in the lower body including the gluteus maximus,

ilopsoas at the front of the hips, hamstring, calf and quadriceps muscles. Arm, shoulder and chest muscles are also used, but to a lesser extent.

■ **Calories** – You will burn around 100 calories per mile – ie around 420 an hour running at a reasonable pace. This will increase by up to three per cent when you add hills and steps.

■ **Bones** – Even a one mile run will stress the bones in your hips and legs in such a way that it helps them retain calcium and ward off the bone thinning disease osteoporosis.

■ **Heart** – Great for the cardiovascular system, running forces the heart and lungs to work more efficiently. Studies have shown that regular running could cut the risk of heart disease and the British Heart Foundation says around 10,000 deaths a year could be prevented if more people took it up.

■ **Joints** – Rather than inflicting wear and tear as was once thought, regular running protects vulnerable joints from damage and pain, found researchers. Adults who run consistently can expect to have 25 per cent less musculoskeletal pain and less arthritis than non-runners when they get older. In a study, people who ran at least six hours per week on average experienced less pain and injuries by the time they were in their 60s and 70s than non runners. The key is to run regularly if you can, as this will allow your joints, tendons, ligaments, discs and muscles to get used to the habitual pounding. The body accommodates and copes with the demands, so that running doesn't necessarily lead to pain.

OUTDOORS V INDOORS

A lack of wind resistance means there is a small decrease in energy expenditure when running on a treadmill which is compounded by the fact that the treadmill belt propels you along slightly. You need to raise the treadmill incline by at least one per cent to expend as many calories as if you were walking or running on a flat pavement outdoors. What's more, treadmills don't have any way to simulate downhill running or turns – something your body's muscles adapt to if you run outside.

RISK FACTOR

Low risk, but it is a good idea to join a running club or to run with a partner if you prefer to tackle more isolated routes.

COST 

ALSO TRY

Track running – There are more than 600 floodlit, all-weather running tracks in the UK most of which are home to Britain's athletics clubs but which are increasingly (and woefully) underused. You don't have to be Linford Christie or Paula Radcliffe to use a track – everyone from carthorses to thoroughbreds is entitled to use them. If you prefer a pre-determined route or distance and don't mind running round in circles, then they make an ideal city-based running venue. Made from a springy rubber, they also have more give than tarmac and concrete so are kinder to the legs.

Both photographs courtesy of sportengland.org/promotingsport

PARK CIRCUITS

A fitness revolution of recent years has been park-based circuits – sometimes called urban bootcamp – an outdoor fitness class in which groups of people are led through gruelling army-style workouts that involve lunging, sprinting and bench-dipping in parks, commons and any open space. In London, the trend was triggered by a company called British Military Fitness, run by former army PT instructors. Expect sprints, throwing weighted medicine balls, mini hurdles and step-ups on park benches. It is so non-stop, there is barely time to remind yourself where you are and what you are doing. Other companies have joined the fray – many gyms now run park-based circuits and Optimal Life Fitness is a company that has incorporated the popularity of Russian kettlebells (heavy weighted implements with a handle that is held to swing the weight around your body) into their circuits.

Image courtesy of British Military Fitness

HOW TO DO IT

Organised circuits (which are charged per session but are surprisingly cheap) generally cover a distance of two or three miles. 'Recruits', as they are termed in many bootcamp circuits, are handed a coloured bib so that they can spot their workout colleagues should they become detached from the group, and are typically taken through a running and stretching warm-up routine. During the circuit proper, you run between conditioning exercises performed every couple of minutes with instructors bellowing mercilessly in your ears should you appear to be slacking. The routine is different each time, so you never know quite what to expect. If you prefer a less structured approach, then you could always make up your own circuit, performing press-ups against trees, bench-dips on park benches and sprinting and jogging around the park's perimeter.

Photograph by Tommy Matthews, outdoor-extreme.com

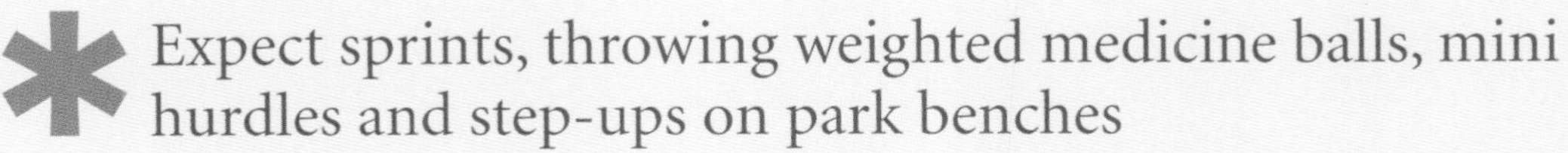

Expect sprints, throwing weighted medicine balls, mini hurdles and step-ups on park benches

EQUIPMENT

A pair of trainers and a tracksuit or similar. Other than that all you need are trees, park benches or walls, grass and tarmac.

BODY BOOSTING

■ **Muscles** – The variety of upper and lower body exercises test every muscle imaginable, but especially the hamstrings, quadriceps and calf muscles in the legs. It will also tax the mind – you might find this approach less tedious than a straightforward run.

■ **Calories** – On average expect to burn between 7.4 and 10.9 calories a minute for this exhaustive form of exercise. Within six weeks you can expect to lose five to six pounds in weight and to lower your body fat percentage (replacing flab with muscle) quite considerably. Several studies have confirmed that circuit training – indoors or out – is the best way to burn calories as it incorporates all essential aspects of fitness.

RISK FACTOR

Since this is basically running punctuated with simple exercises and is performed in parks away from traffic, the risks are low. If you choose a class with kettlebells, be careful not to drop them on your feet or to attempt lifting a weight too heavy for your level of fitness, as this could cause muscular strain.

COST  

All images courtesy of British Military Fitness

50
43
44
24

IN-LINE SKATING

Often called roller-blading (a trademarked name for a brand of skates), this sport has become the epitome of a cool form of transport for thousands of commuters and couriers alike. In many cities its appeal now extends beyond getting from A to B. Mass skating events – such as the PariRoller staged every Friday evening through the streets of Paris, attracting 10,000 people – and similar group skates in Amsterdam and London have transformed in-line skating into a boom sport. Like joggers taking part in fun runs, many skaters find that the social aspect of these mass events spurs them onto covering greater distances. However, if you prefer to go solo or in smaller groups, always check that in-line skating is permitted in your local park – some councils ban it for fear of collisions with pedestrians.

HOW TO DO IT

It's not as difficult as it looks. Most people can grasp the basics of in-line skating within a couple of hours, even if they have never previously tried it. The biggest barrier is a fear of falling over, as much for the embarrassment it causes as the pain. By far the most common technical error among beginners is a failure to bend the knees. As in skiing, the shins should be pressed forward against the front of the boot and knees should be slightly in front of the toes. Feet should be hip-width apart and, once you have mastered scooting along – roll, then push to the side with one leg before lifting the same leg back in and repeating on the other leg – turning and other moves will seem less of a mountain to climb.

EQUIPMENT

If you are new to in-line skating, it is advisable to hire skates until you decide it is for you. If you do decide to buy, it is best to visit a specialist skate shop that will advise on the most appropriate pair for your size, ability and budget. You will also need protective wrist guards, knee and elbow pads. Some skaters wear helmets for added safety.

BODY BOOSTING

■ **Muscles** – In-line skating is a low impact activity (meaning it is kind to vulnerable joints and bones) and can leave you with a strong, toned core section that helps to improve balance posture and prevent back pain. It will also give your leg muscles a good workout.

Both images courtesy of Skatefresh

INSTRUCTO
skatefresh

Photograph by Tom Jenkins

■ **Calories** – Gliding along on skates is not something that will get you superfit. Sports physiologists claim it will not tax your heart enough to push you into what is known as 'the training zone' – when your body produces an aerobic response – and therefore won't burn many calories (probably around 200 an hour). However, the more adept a skater you become, the harder you can push yourself and you will begin to feel as well as look fitter. Add some squats, circling and other exercises and your calories burned will increase to at least 425 per hour.

RISK FACTOR

Medium. Inevitably, there will be falls, especially when you are learning to skate, but since most skating will be done off-road, the dangers are low once you master the technique. In fact, in-line skating is shown to be safer than cycling – 3.4 injuries per 1,000 skaters say the stats. Lessons are recommended to minimise the damage.

COST  

ALSO TRY

Ice skating – Outdoor ice-rinks are a relatively new phenomenon in the UK, but one that has taken hold with such gusto, that they are undoubtedly here to stay. Come autumn, outdoor rinks are set up in around 20 venues from the Eden Project in Cornwall to Glasgow's George Square. London has eight winter rinks in places as picturesque as Somerset House and Kew Gardens. With many open until midnight, you can skate beneath the stars (and floodlights) and there are few outdoor sports that could be considered as romantic or emotionally pleasing an experience. Although they cater for all abilities and members of staff circle the rink in hawk-fashion looking for casualties, it is wise to have some lessons, or at least practices, before you join the masses. You won't break into the kind of sweat you will when running, but be prepared for aching thighs and calves when you leave the ice.

Photograph by David Levene

ULTIMATE

Think soccer with a flying disc, or Frisbee (a trademarked name), replacing a ball and without a referee dictating the flow of the game and you have an idea what the game of Ultimate is about. Created by a group of students from Columbia High School in New Jersey in the late 1960s, it now has something of a cult following around the world. Played on a 70 by 40 yard section of a football pitch marked with end zones, the aim of the seven-a-side game is to keep the Frisbee moving by throwing it downfield (you cannot run with the disc) until a teammate catches it in the opponent's end zone to score a point. The first team to amass 13-21 points (depending on the level of tournament) wins. Top level games can last up to two hours.

HOW TO DO IT

Beginners need not feel intimidated when they turn up to play for the first time – Ultimate is a game that appeals to all ages, abilities and genders. Technique, say proponents, is far more important than strength or size. During a match, any player holding the Frisbee has ten seconds in which to pass it on to another team member. If the Frisbee hasn't moved after ten seconds, possession is automatically handed to the opposition.

EQUIPMENT

A flying disc, of course, and a team. Although you can play ad-hoc Ultimate in the local park, your best bet is to join a club where coaching and tournaments are arranged.

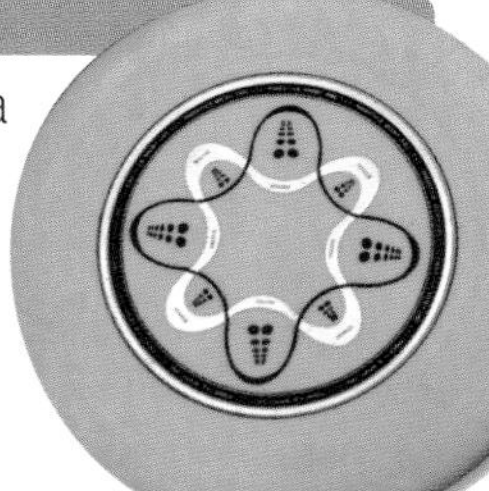

There is a governing body for the sport – the World Flying Disc Federation – and an estimated 100,000 people play in countries across the world. In the UK alone, there are more than 42 affiliated clubs. Details can be found in the directory from page 192.

BODY BOOSTING

■ **Muscles** – Both the calf and thigh muscles are heavily recruited during the running phase of Ultimate, but the jumping also engages the buttocks and core muscles around the midriff.

■ **Calories** – Because you are sprinting up and down the pitch for much of a game, expect to burn at least 450 calories an hour.

■ **Bones** – Ultimate involves a lot of jumping to grab the air-bound flying disc and the constant leaping and landing is an excellent way to strengthen bones in the hips, spine and legs.

Both photographs by Mark Earley

* Do not expect this to be anything like throwing a Frisbee to your dog in the park

RISK FACTOR

Do not expect this to be anything like throwing a Frisbee to your dog in the park. Injuries from twisting or turning at speed are commonplace, as are grass burns incurred from diving for a catch. Since flying discs have a will of their own, there is also a risk of being hit as it drops with the wind. But don't be put off – this game is the ultimate in fun.

COST 

TAI CHI

A martial art unlike any other, Tai (meaning ultimate or supreme) Chi (meaning energy) is characterised by its slow, precise and flowing movements which make it as far removed from the sweat and grind of the gym as can be imagined. However, for all its gentleness, it is known to produce more health-giving benefits than many more vigorous types of exercise. Traditionally used as a form of combat, practitioners claim its moves are more defensive than offensive and that the meditative calm it induces is as beneficial for mind as body. These factors account for Tai Chi's ever expanding popularity. In China, where it has been practised for thousands of years, it is estimated that more than 200 million people incorporate Tai Chi postures and moves into their everyday lives, and in the UK a growing number of gyms and health clubs are including it in their timetables.

HOW TO DO IT

Tai Chi comprises 108 main postures and, according to the principles of Chinese medicine on which it is based, each of its intricate movements aims to restore balance in the body's opposing energy forces, or yin and yang. For full benefits, it is recommended that at least some of the postures are practised daily.

EQUIPMENT

Best practised in bare feet on springy grass, you need nothing but loose-fitting clothing and a relaxed, open mind. Lessons are advisable initially as you will need to learn the movements – each class contains elements of posture, breathing and concentration. A Tai Chi session usually lasts around 20-40 minutes.

BODY BOOSTING

■ **Muscles** – Tai Chi has similar benefits to running when it comes to improving the leg muscles, a study found. Researchers looked at the strength and endurance of leg muscles as well as flexibility in knee, ankle and hip joints in subjects aged 60 and over who were sedentary or had regularly practised either Tai Chi or jogging. Each of the activities had comparable positive effects, although Tai Chi practitioners had the strongest knee joints of all.

■ **Calories** – If it's fat burning you are after, don't look to Tai Chi. Expect to burn only around 200 calories an hour.

■ **Balance** – The slow and gentle movements are known to improve balance and coordination, thereby preventing falls. A study of 78 year-olds who were prone to falling significantly improved their strength, balance and stability with a 12-week course of Tai Chi.

Photograph by Ronnie Robinson

Photograph by Ronnie Robinson

- **Mind** – Tai Chi has been shown to have a positive effect on people suffering from depression, anxiety and stress. Top sports people are increasingly using the precise movements to boost their concentration and focus. Tiger Woods reportedly practised Tai Chi as a young golfer growing up in Los Angeles and Catherina McKiernan, former London Marathon winner, has trained to teach Chi Running (see right).
- **Health problems** – A review of 47 studies looking at the impact Tai Chi had on people with chronic health problems like heart disease or multiple sclerosis, showed it had undoubted benefits including improved balance control and flexibility. One study found that regular classes gave patients who had suffered heart failure better movement, and reduced the potential for recurrence.

RISK FACTOR

Very low.

COST   

ALSO TRY

Chi Running – a combination of Tai Chi and running created by Danny Dreyer, a running coach and Tai Chi practitioner based in San Francisco, it teaches a technique of relaxation in motion and encourages lowering your perception of effort, regardless of how fast you are going. Chi running takes some practice. It involves leaning forward from the heels (not the waist or hips), and allowing the body to work with – rather than against – gravity. Proponents claim there is more to it than simply tweaking your running style to avoid injuries, but that you need to actively engage your core muscles, as well as your mind, producing both mental and physical benefits.

Photograph by Lori A. Chung, www.thepetphotographer.com

BUGGY WORKOUTS

In America, the rise in popularity of buggy, stroller or pushchair workouts among new mothers (and some fathers) has been meteoric. What began with individuals seeking a means to getting fit while power-walking or jogging with their baby has mushroomed into an industry with classes such as Buggy Fit and Strollercise being held in parks on both sides of the Atlantic. An undoubted attraction is the sociability of these sessions. Australian researchers found that among women diagnosed with post-natal depression, those who completed a 12-week stroller class showed fewer symptoms than those in a sedentary mother and baby group. It was, concluded the researchers, meeting other stroller-walking mothers combined with the aerobic activity's ability to raise levels of endorphins, that produced the benefits.

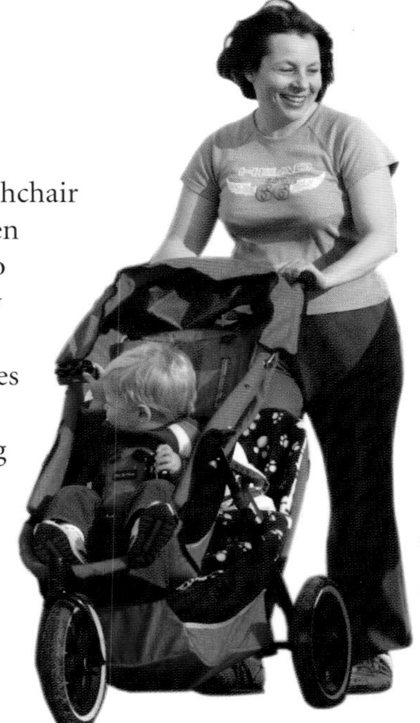

Image courtesy of Buggyfit

HOW TO DO IT

Unless you are prepared to leave them in a crèche while you work out at the gym, having a baby does limit your fitness regimen somewhat. Buggy workouts are the perfect solution. They can be performed solo, but organised group classes will often provide a much-needed social outlet for new parents. Most classes are based around a circuit that includes some running or power-walking, lunges, press-ups and other strengthening exercises all performed with or next to your pushchair. How fast you go depends on factors such as fitness, mummy-fat – the extra weight that many women carry after childbirth – and the age and size of your baby, but raising the heart rate and getting breathless is the overall aim.

EQUIPMENT

A pair of running or walking shoes, a tracksuit and a supportive sports bra, especially if breast-feeding, are the basics. For basic buggy workouts on tarmac and concrete surfaces, a reasonably sturdy but lightweight buggy will suffice. Check that the handlebars are at a comfortable height and that the wheels are not positioned in a way that can trip you up. Pushchairs should be easy to handle but also have some suspension to keep the baby comfortable. A more specialist stroller is a

> ✱ Organised group classes will often provide a much needed social outlet for new parents

worthwhile investment if you plan to go off-road frequently or if you plan to run rather than walk with your child. There are buggy-based fun runs and road races organised around the country and if these appeal, you will definitely need a stroller with plenty of suspension, added traction tyres and bigger wheels.

BODY BOOSTING

■ **Muscles** – Pushing a buggy is like weight training in itself, and will make good use of your hamstring, gluteus and calf muscles as well as those in the upper body. Stops are often made to perform abdominal-strengthening exercises and most sessions focus on exercises to strengthen the pelvic floor, which is weakened through the physical effort of childbirth. Particular emphasis is placed on body parts that are overused in the care of a young baby. The moment a woman has a baby she is bending upwards of 100 times a day, putting strain on the back. This is compounded by the fact that the baby is getting heavier every day: in six months the baby's body weight has doubled. Daily movements with the baby add to the bodily demands – think of a car seat and the fact that a mother is turning to face the baby while also keeping her eyes on the road. That action places a lot of stress on the rotator cuff muscles in the shoulders, which are among those that are worked.

■ **Calories** – Around 450 per hour. Many women lose half a stone in a month.

RISK FACTOR

Exercising before, during and after pregnancy has wrongly been perceived as a risky approach for many years. In fact, a study of more than 150,000 women carried out by exercise physiologists at the University of St Louis and published in the journal *Medicine and Science*, found that the majority of expectant and new mums did not meet even the minimum requirement of daily activity (30 minutes of cumulative exercise) needed to stay healthy. Of course, it is vital to get the all-clear from the medical professionals who are overseeing your progress before you embark on a fitness regimen after giving birth, and women who have undergone a caesarian will have to wait longer, but joining a class with an instructor specifically trained to deal with post-childbirth fitness issues is the best step you can take.

COST  

Image courtesy of Buggyfit

buggyfit

RECUMBENT CYCLING

If you haven't seen one – and if you have you would remember – the recumbent bike is, as its name suggests, a bicycle that has been rotated 180 degrees. With three wheels (two wheelers are also available but are less common), the pedals are up where the front wheel should be, the seat is down where the pedals should be and the rider is half-sitting, half-lying down. This mode of transport certainly has not become popular because of its cool appearance. Yet Britain seems to be following in the recumbent tracks of America, where sales of these bikes have doubled to almost 60,000 in recent years. The main attraction of recumbents for city dwellers (apart from the obvious lack of saddle soreness) is that they move incredibly quickly through traffic – these bikes are banned from conventional races because they are too speedy. Even the most basic of these low leaning bikes can reach speeds of 55 mph on flat ground and the world record for a human powered land vehicle is set by a recumbent cyclist at a speed of almost 70 mph.

HOW TO DO IT

Most hire shops offer lessons and advise starting out on a recumbent in an off-road setting such as a local park just to get used to their idiosyncrasies. Most of the bikes are operated via hand-held brakes and to move faster you simply push your back further into the seat, allowing your legs more range of movement. Turning can be tricky to grasp, made cumbersome because of the wide-spread wheels and you need to allow some distance between your bike and the curb as you sweep round corners. Even with the rear-wheel suspension that is fitted on most of the latest models, the fact that you are positioned so close to the ground means that you tend to feel the reverberations from every bump and pothole.

EQUIPMENT

Medium level recumbent bikes are not cheap (costing upwards of £500), so it is worthwhile hiring one first to see if you are bitten by the bug.

BODY BOOSTING

■ **Calories** – Depending on how tough the route and how fast you cycle, a recumbent could burn between 360 and 510 calories an hour.

■ **Muscles** – Research at the State University of New York showed that while muscle usage is much the same as with regular cycling (ie working all the major muscles in the legs), the focus is altogether different. On recumbent bikes, your hamstring and gluteus muscles work harder than your quadriceps, which makes it great for firming your bottom. The seated position also means that your knees,

shoulders and neck are under less strain than they are in the hunched position of a traditional bike which is good news for anyone prone to back or neck pain.

■ **Circulation** – Because the rider's legs are raised to near heart level, researchers have shown that blood flows more easily to the heart. This physiological effect has also been linked to increased endurance. Anecdotally, recumbent riders also say that their more upright upper body posture allows for easier breathing.

RISK FACTOR

It is worth bearing in mind that the bike's low profile means that you are virtually invisible to cars which is why many riders attach tall flags to the backs of their seats so that they can be spotted. Your vision of the road is also restricted by your position, and it is very difficult to look over your shoulder at traffic behind you. This can be partially remedied by affixing side mirrors to your handlebars.

COST £   

BOWLS

It is fair to say that, to date, lawn bowls' public image has hardly been one of athleticism and youthfulness. Once cruelly described as a cross between a sport and an afternoon nap, its participants have always seemed somewhat more grandparent than Olympian, not helped, it must be said, by their uniform of starchy white skirts and blazers, nor by the fact that a brand of denture fixing cream was once a major sponsor of the game. However, this previously genteel sport is quietly undergoing a radical transformation. No longer the sole preserve of the grey army, there are two million people in the UK who play regularly and a growing number are in their teens, 20s or 30s. Furthermore, the game has been given a modern twist thanks in part to an influx of fashion-conscious young female players at the top level. British player Carol Ashby, the first woman ever to beat a man in a major international indoor bowls event, sports numerous piercings, a tattoo, and flattering white pedal pushers. A youth development scheme by the English Bowling Association has established several regional schools of excellence where budding young players are encouraged to reach their potential.

HOW TO DO IT

Bowls is played on a 34-40 metre square green surrounded by a ditch to catch stray bowls. It is a precision sport, related to petanque, in which players take turns to bowl as close as possible to a small white ball, called the 'jack', which is rolled at least 23 metres away. Once all bowls have been played, a competitor or team gets one point for each of their bowls that is closer to the jack than their opponent's. Direction of play is reversed to complete a game.

Because bowls are not quite round – they are shaved on one side to give them a bias – players must learn techniques which best take advantage of the way the ball curves in the direction of the bias.

EQUIPMENT

With almost 3,000 bowls clubs in England alone – most offering free taster sessions to beginners – there are plenty of places to have a trial session where equipment is supplied. Sets of bowls vary in price according to weight but it is worth investing in a set if you are to play regularly.

Clubs and competitions impose dress rules although these were recently relaxed to allow women to wear trousers, coloured shirts and baseball caps. Gloves are no longer required.

Image courtesy of Bowls England

No longer the sole preserve of the grey army, there are two million people in the UK who play regularly

BODY BOOSTING

■ **Muscles** – A survey of 2,200 players aged 15-80 showed that nine out of 10 believe it keeps their muscles fit and supple, most likening the effects to yoga. Muscles in the arms, chest and waist (from bending to bowl) are among those targeted to the greatest effect.

■ **Calories** – Not a great calorie burner; you might expect to use 150-180 an hour in a game of bowls.

RISK FACTOR

A study by Monash University's accident research centre in Australia found that bowls players do incur injuries – often strains from slipping or accidents from dropping heavy bowls onto the feet. These can largely be avoided by a thorough warm up and cool down.

COST   

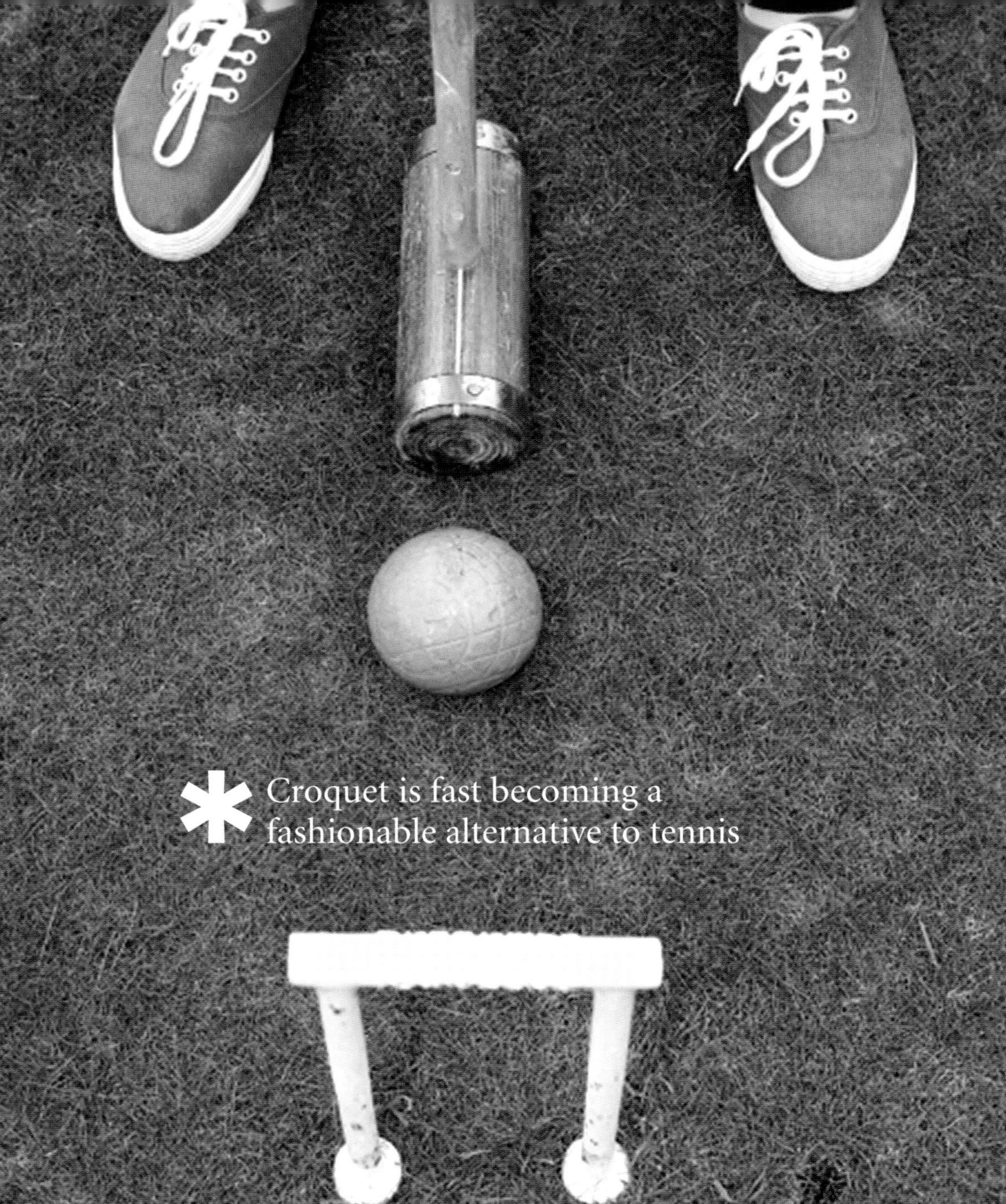

* Croquet is fast becoming a fashionable alternative to tennis

CROQUET

Croquet is an ancient game that dates back to the 14th century, which requires players to hit balls using mallets through small hoops set into a grass playing field. It has always been perceived as a gentle sport for mature members of the aristocracy, played only by the well-heeled on manicured lawns in genteel surroundings. However, The Croquet Association in the UK has made much headway in changing this image. Today, even gyms have started staging croquet tournaments during the summer months, and it is fast becoming a fashionable alternative to tennis.

HOW TO DO IT

Two forms of the game are generally played at competitive level. Association or Tournament Croquet, the more difficult to learn, is played to international level while a simpler version, golf croquet, is much easier to pick up.

Hitting a ball with the flat end of a mallet, the basic technique in croquet, is surprisingly easy, once you master the golden rule of not lifting your head when you take a shot (otherwise the ball goes hurtling off track). The objective is to keep your ball in play for as long as possible, either by hitting it through a hoop (which gains you a point and an extra stroke) or by performing what is known as a 'roquet' shot in which your ball hits another ball and earns you two free strokes. You must follow a set course, going through each of the hoops twice on the way round and on the way back.

Photograph by David Sillitoe

EQUIPMENT

You will need a croquet set, but they are inexpensive – you can buy a whole set for four players for under £100. Lessons are a great idea as they help you to understand the rules and to improve technique. Either join a croquet club or take a course at the local gym or health club.

BODY BOOSTING

■ **Muscles** – Croquet is not the most vigorous of sports, but with the right technique you will use a sequence of muscles – first the thigh muscles, then back, forearm and hand muscles. Poor technique means the hand muscles are used almost in isolation.

■ **Calories** – Expect to burn an average of 160 calories an hour.

RISK FACTOR

Barring any mishaps with the mallet, risks are low.

COST  

KORFBALL

This game, first played in Holland at the beginning of the 20th century, loosely incorporates the best aspects of basketball and netball with the main difference being that it is a game designed to be played in mixed sex teams, with four men and four women on each side. Each participant is 'paired' with a player of the same sex and of roughly equal height from the opposing team, and the aim is to pass the ball from teammate to teammate, until someone is in a position to shoot into the 'korf' – a wicker basket suspended from a post. Its popularity has spread to such an extent that it is played in more than 40 countries.

HOW TO DO IT

A pitch is divided into two sections. Half a team (two men and two women) attacks and the other four defend. Each attacking player is hounded by their 'paired' defender from the opposition. Unlike netball, anyone can shoot for goal from anywhere within their half of the pitch and there is no rule which states your foot has to be drilled to the floor when you pass, meaning that you can swivel and turn to make the best move. But, unlike basketball, you can't run or dribble with the ball. You also have to be something of a jack of all trades since, after every two goals, players swap positions so that attackers become defenders and vice versa.

EQUIPMENT

Join a club and coaching, competitions and training will be included in the relatively low cost of your membership fee. All equipment – including the korf nets and ball – similar in size and weight to a netball – are also provided.

BODY BOOSTING

■ **Calories** – A game lasts 30 minutes each way – much of which is spent running around and jumping – which means you burn a total of up to 600 calories.

■ **Coordination** – Hand-eye coordination, reaction times, speed and flexibility all improve with regular korfball playing.

RISK FACTOR

As with any game that involves jumping and reaching for a ball, there is a danger of twisted ankles through a poor landing. However, that aside, the likelihood of injury in korfball is low.

COST £ £

Photograph by Katie Ellis

Photograph by Jacqueline Hoare, englandkorfball.co.uk

SKATEBOARDING

Photograph by Tina Stallard, courtesy of Natural England

If you are one of the many people who consigned your skateboard to the garden shed once you grew out of your teens then there has never been a better time to dust off your wheels for some urban surfing again. About 600,000 people in Britain skateboard regularly and, of those, a growing number are taking it up for the first time in their mid-20s and 30s. One third of skateboard owners in the UK are now women.

HOW TO DO IT

Skateboarding is more physically demanding than you might think – even at the most basic level, effort is called for to push yourself along. Progress to jumps and turns and you will require strength, agility, balance and coordination. Unfortunately, there is no short cut from wobbling precariously along the footpaths of your local park to achieving the 900-degree somersaults of the pros. Even top riders start by sitting on a board and rolling around. Lessons are hard to come by, but you might find some instruction on offer at a local skatepark.

EQUIPMENT

You can buy a basic board reasonably cheaply – experienced riders construct their own. You will also need protective gear such as wrist, hand and knee guards as well as a helmet.

BODY BOOSTING

- **Calories** – Skateboarding is on a par with gentle cycling and burns about 350 calories an hour.
- **Muscles** – Calf, hamstring and quadriceps muscles become super-strong as most manoeuvres require you to engage the legs.

RISK FACTOR

Knee injuries from landing badly and hyper-extended elbows from supporting yourself as you fall are the most common injuries when people begin to experiment with tricks. There is also a risk that one leg becomes stronger than the other if you always use the same foot to propel you along the ground. In the long term, favouring one leg can leave you prone to postural imbalances, so practise Tai Chi or other strengthening exercises to balance things out.

COST  

Photograph by Tom Jenkins

SKATEBOARDING JARGON YOU SHOULD KNOW

180 or 360 – refers to the number of degrees covered in a jump.
Fakie – riding the board backwards.
Flip-trick – spinning the board on any of its axes.
Deck – the flat bit of the board that you stand on.
Trucks – the metal attachments which house the axels and connect the wheel to the deck.
Goofy foot – skating with your right foot forward.
Grinding –jumping onto a bench or curb and sliding along it, scraping your trucks. There are different types of grinds including crooked, nose-grind and 50-50.
Nollie – short for a 'nose ollie'. Using your front foot to smack the front of your board against the ground while your back foot pulls the board up into the air.

FREE RUNNING/PARKOUR

If any activity embraces the urban landscape to the full, it is Free Running or Parkour. Buildings, fences, walls and lampposts become at once obstacles and facilitators of movement, as you scramble, climb, leap and vault over them, moving through the city with a fluidity of motion akin to dance. Exponents – known as traceurs – revel in the interaction between the human body and the man-made environment, and describe the process more as a mindset than a sport. The man widely credited with founding the activity is David Belle, who began practising it as a teenager in the built-up Parisian suburb of Lisses, finding freedom by breaking through the physical constraints of his surroundings. A BBC trailer called *Rush Hour* introduced Parkour to wider audience in the UK. In the film, Belle was shown crossing a gridlocked city – at one point, leaping from building to building 60 metres above a street.

HOW TO DO IT

Take an obstacle, climb, scramble or jump over it to the next obstacle and then to the next – let your imagination run riot and you are free-running. However, it is about more than just crazy leaps – Parkour encourages participants to channel their energies into becoming focused, graceful individuals. There are no rules as such, but some moves such as cat leaps, tic tacs and vaults have become standard. Repetitive drills and taking things slowly is the only way to master them. Urban Freeflow, one of the leading Parkour networks with about 14,000 members worldwide, runs workshops to give beginners the chance to learn the basics in a soft environment.

EQUIPMENT

All you need are long trousers, long sleeves and a pair of cushioned trainers. Oh, and one big imagination.

BODY BOOSTING

■ **Muscles** One of few sports to test every muscle in the body. The more accomplished a traceur you become, the wider range of muscles you will engage as you leap, swing, scramble, hop and run across and between buildings, steps, fences and rooftops.

■ **Calories** – You will burn at least 412 calories an hour, but top free runners can burn as many as 600 in that time.

RISK FACTOR

Potentially huge. This is one of the riskiest of all sports for the ill-informed beginner. Many medical and health organisations, including the Royal Society for the Prevention of Accidents have issued cautionary warnings, advising anyone considering taking it up to get advice from experts and not to attempt copycat moves.

COST £

CINEMA

CHAPTER 2

WILD GYM IN THE WATER

Moon River, wider than a mile,
I'm crossing you in style some day.
Oh, dream maker, you heart breaker,
Wherever you're going I'm going your way
Johnny Mercer, lyricist
Image courtesy of the Countryside Alliance

Water: there is so much more to it than chlorinated pools. And, living on an island, we have a greater scope to explore and enjoy it than many. However, there are many who are yet to be convinced that water-based activities are worth trying – believing it is likely to be unbearably cold and that British waterways are at best murky, and at worst sewage-ridden with the odd dead animal floating along for company. But these are misnomers. Rivers and lakes in the UK are cleaner than they have been for 150 years – about 75 per cent are safe to swim in. Even the River Thames is not nearly as dirty as one might imagine – in fact, the upper, non-tidal part of the Thames is at its cleanest in living memory with salmon, otters and kingfishers on some stretches.
As for water temperatures, rivers often reach around 20-27 degrees in the summer months.

If you need further reassurance, the Environment Agency rates rivers and lakes on a scale of A to E in terms of their cleanliness, and a quick click onto their website can determine whether your nearest is safe. Only those on top of Snowdon or similarly remote places have water pure enough to be listed as

A-grade, but there are plenty of B and C-listed waters that are perfect for water activities. It is wise to check with the agency for contaminants, although problems are rare. The main ones to be aware of are blue-green algae, which is dangerous if ingested (it's usually visible when it's in high-risk quantities) and Weil's Disease, also known as leptospirosis, which occurs in animals such as rats, but can be transmitted to humans through contaminated urine in rivers. These and other possible risks will be clearly listed on the agency's website. Considering the value of much of the equipment needed to participate in many water sports, it can be surprisingly cheap to access at registered outdoor centres, and safety clothing is also generally provided as part of the cost of a lesson.

A few final words of advice if you do fancy trying one of the activities in this chapter – always check that a centre provides instructors that are affiliated to a governing body or association to ensure safety and teaching standards are met, and that the centre itself has some form of public liability insurance that will cover you if you are involved in an accident. Otherwise, there is little to stop you from diving in.

OUTDOOR SWIMMING

Outdoor swimming has long been associated with that batty bunch who plunge into the Serpentine in Hyde Park on New Year's day, Lycra-clad triathletes or cross-Channel swimmers. But a new breed of outdoor swimmer is challenging that stereotype by claiming it can be more pleasurable than running and more soul-soothing than yoga. To many, swimming in pools is boring. You count length after length and then get out. With no lane dividers, no turning every 25-50 metres, no one getting in your way and no plasters floating past your nose, the attractions of switching to the outdoors start to become clear.

HOW TO DO IT

If you can swim, you can swim outdoors. However, if you are used to diving in at your local pool or are not particularly confident in your ability, it is wise to build up your exposure to the water outside for five minutes at a time to get used to it. For a gentle introduction to the outdoors, try lidos – there are 12 in London alone – or join one of the Outdoor Swimming Society's introductory swims. Once you gain confidence you can graduate to ponds, lakes and rivers or even the open sea. You could also try an outdoor swimming holiday package from a company such as SwimTrek, which offers excursions in venues as diverse as the Scottish Inner Hebrides and Greek Cyclades (see directory).

Studies in the UK and America show that 67 per cent of people who can swim are afraid of deep water because they feel out of control. If this rings true for you, then stroke improver classes could boost your confidence and competence several-fold. A classic mistake is to swim with your head pulled back out of the water, placing undue stress on the neck and spine, and eventually causing pain if you swim regularly. For every inch the head is lifted, the hips sink two inches, meaning you swim more slowly and less efficiently.

EQUIPMENT

If the water is likely to be cool, there are precautions you can take to prevent shivering. Body fat determines how long someone can withstand cold water, but it is not a precise measure. Other factors that lower your tolerance to chilly temperatures include alcohol consumption the previous day, general health and food intake (you need to eat regular, small, high-carbohydrate snacks beforehand – the rule about not eating an hour before you swim is a myth, although you should avoid heavy meals). Wetsuits can also help – the Amateur Swimming Association rules state that they must be worn in open-water competitions once the temperature drops below 14 degrees – but outside of competitive swims, the decision about what to wear (or not) is down to you.

Main photograph by Dominick Tyler

* A new breed of outdoor swimmer is challenging stereotypes by claiming it can be more pleasurable than running and more soul-soothing than yoga

BODY BOOSTING

■ **Muscles** – Swimming is one of the best all-body sports, recruiting most major muscles with each stroke. Water acts as a giant cushion for the body and is kind to joints and tendons. The deeper you wade into water, the lighter your body comes. American research has shown that waist-deep water reduces the pressure on joints by 50 per cent, chest-deep by 75 per cent, and if you work out in water up to neck level, as with swimming, your bodyweight is effectively reduced by as much as 90 per cent. This means aqua-activity is particularly good for people with vulnerable joints, arthritis or osteoporosis as the water supports their bodies.

■ **Calories** – Swimming front crawl in an indoor pool will burn 250-300 calories in half an hour; add the extra calories burned simply to stay warm and the extra energy sometimes needed to cope with waves, currents and the elements and you are looking at considerably more.

RISK FACTOR

There are undeniable risks of swimming outdoors. Water is unpredictable, and if you venture out of lakes, lidos and ponds into rivers, seas and oceans, it is paramount that you initially do so with company, preferably that of an experienced club or organised tour. According to the Royal Society for the Prevention of Accidents, around 15 people drown in swimming pools each year, while 356 die in open water. Having said that, only 19 of the deaths in open water were known to be swimming accidents – the most common cause of death is falling in or alcohol-related accidents.

COST  

Photograph by Zillah Crosby of Art of Swimming

ALSO TRY

The Shaw Method – Created by British coach Steven Shaw, the approach uses the postural awareness principles of the Alexander Technique to improve stroke efficiency and the ease with which someone moves through the water. Rather than thrashing out breathless lengths of a pool, the aim is to achieve a graceful swimming style that will put less strain on your body. Courses are held both indoors and out at pools around the UK and abroad. The ultimate result is that you will be able to swim for longer because you exert less effort with each stroke.

ROWING

To many Britons, a rower is somebody who comes out every four years to win the Olympics. Recreational rowing formed a part of most rowing clubs' agenda until about 30 years ago, and although it remained hugely popular in countries such as Germany and Holland, it fell out of favour at UK clubs when competitive rowing took over. But rowing is not all about tough competition and winning races. Today the Amateur Rowing Association reports a resurgence in the number of people rowing for fun, undoubtedly inspired to take to the water by the success (and physiques) of Britain's gold medal rowers such as Sir Steve Redgrave, James Cracknell and Matthew Pinsent. Clubs in the UK encourage all abilities and ages to join for both competitive and fitness reasons.

HOW TO DO IT

Join a club affiliated to the Amateur Rowing Association (or the Scottish and Welsh equivalents) and you will get free tuition and use of equipment as well as access to a packed competitive and social agenda.

Basic technique involves keeping the back upright and the head, neck and arms relaxed throughout a stroke. Push strongly with the legs and rock the body gently forward from the hips. On the return stroke, do not allow the knees to lift until the oar has passed them on approach to the waist.

EQUIPMENT

Clubs – which are cheap to join – will provide you with all the equipment and instruction you need to start. If you later decide that this is the sport for you, you might then choose to purchase your own boat or indoor rowing machine, called an ergometer – the preferred method of training for elite rowers during winter months. Most regular rowers wear club strips – tight fitting all-in-one garments – and while it is not necessary to don something quite so figure-hugging, it is important to avoid baggy clothing that could catch in your oars or get stuck in your slide when you row.

BODY BOOSTING

■ **Muscles** – The classic build of a top rower is broad shouldered with long, muscular limbs and very low body fat. Like distance runners, they have a high aerobic capacity and are capable of taking in up to 300 litres of air a minute. Although rowers' musculature can make them heavy, the water buoys their boat so it is less of an issue when it comes to moving through water.

Photograph by Tom Jenkins

■ **Calories** – Rowing puts more muscles and joints through a wider range of motion than any other sport – knees, hips, arms and shoulders will each move through 90-130 degrees of rotation in every stroke – and this means that rowing gobbles up more calories than you would use running or cycling for the same length of time. Even slow rowing burns 400 calories an hour. Pick up the pace and you could burn 600 or more.

■ **Spine** – A study carried out on male rowers, triathletes and sedentary controls found that rowers had significantly higher bone mass density (BMD) in the spine, an area traditionally vulnerable to osteoporosis. Another study on 14 female rowers showed that in addition to the higher BMD, during a six-minute race, the muscular pull forces generated in the spine were equivalent to 4.6 times body weight – a figure that compares favourably with that attained during weight training, which is widely considered as one of the very best bone building exercises.

■ **Joints** – Rowing is a non-weight bearing exercise so there is less pressure on the knees and hips than if you were pounding away on the roads.

RISK FACTOR

A lot of people pick up appallingly bad rowing technique on indoor rowing machines at gyms. They use an aggressive movement with an arched back that is nothing like the technique used by Olympic rowers. The result is spinal curvature and a lot of tension through the neck. It is vital to learn good technique with a qualified coach or instructor at a registered club. Capsizing is obviously also a risk. The Water Safety Code requires rowers to wear a lifejacket or buoyancy aid and any sold in the UK should have an EN (European Standard Number).

COST 

Both images courtesy of sportengland.org/promotingsport

WERNER

CANOEING/KAYAKING

Although there is a difference between a canoe and a kayak – the former is an open boat in which a single paddle is generally used, while kayaking, the more common of the sports and an Olympic discipline, uses a closed vessel and double-bladed paddle – the two are often grouped together under the umbrella term canoeing. More than 500,000 people now canoe regularly in the UK, an increase of 25 per cent in the last few years, making this one of the country's fastest growing sports. For many of those who paddle regularly, it is purely a recreational pursuit to be dabbled with on sunny weekends, but with 100,000 young people being introduced to the sport through schools and the Duke of Edinburgh award scheme every year, an increasing number are progressing through to the competitive ranks of canoeing.

HOW TO DO IT

You will need to be a reasonably strong swimmer before you start, as falling in is an unavoidable part of the learning process. However, with the help of a few lessons, the basic technique can be picked up quite quickly – and you will be taught how to capsize safely (and to recover from it) early on.

Canoeing and kayaking have a similar paddle technique. In a kayak, begin paddling by leaning slightly forward – a backward lean or slouch places unnecessary weight at the back of the boat, minimising your control. Holding the paddle correctly is essential – your hands should be positioned either side of its midpoint so that your elbows form right angles. Keep the right hand fixed tightly at all times. Reach forward for a long stroke and make sure the whole blade enters the water before you pull backwards. Try to keep the boat level in the water.

At clubs affiliated to the British Canoe Union (BCU) you can try anything from a leisurely tour along rivers and lakes to the Olympic disciplines of sprint racing and slalom canoeing. And if that doesn't float your boat (or kayak), there is always wild-water racing – a test against river and clock with events categorised according to the toughness of the water course.

EQUIPMENT

The most cost-effective way to start is to join a club where equipment and tuition will be provided. Join the BCU and you will also get a license to use 4,500 km of Britain's inland waterways (not all of which are open to the public). If you decide the sport is for

Photographs courtesy of Plas y Brenin, pyb.co.uk

you, you will need to invest in the basic equipment, which, in addition to the boat, includes a paddle, spray deck (an elasticated skirt which prevents water from entering the canoe), a helmet and a buoyancy aid. Clothing is largely weather-dependent – layers are best and long trousers are better than short as the boat can rub on your knees and cause chaffing. Trainers or aqua shoes are fine, although some canoeists prefer to practise barefoot.

BODY BOOSTING

- **Upper body** – With all of its twisting, canoeing is one of the best ways to tone the core muscles that wrap around the waist like a corset including the oblique muscles and the deeply embedded transversus abdominus. It also works the arm and chest muscles as you paddle.
- **Calories** – On average you will burn between 120 and 140 calories for every half an hour spent canoeing. Studies have shown that after 12 weeks of training, top-level canoeists had very low levels of body fat.
- **Heart** – Researchers found that the average mass of the heart's left chamber was 50 per cent greater in canoeists than in non-exercisers.

RISK FACTOR

Like all water sports, there is an inherent danger in taking to a boat and tackling unpredictable conditions. It is best to join a club affiliated to the BCU as you will automatically get third party liability insurance for any accidents that occur.

Image courtesy of Plas y Brenin, pyb.co.uk

BEACH RUNNING/WALKING

Beach Bootcamps are big crowd pullers in the gyms of Florida, LA and Hawaii. But you don't need to be basking in sunshine or even on holiday to reap the benefits of running or walking on sand. The beaches of Britain are uniquely beautiful and very accessible.

Unlike running on firmer surfaces – such as a grass field, running track or tarmac, sand provides no rebound. This means that with each stride your muscles have to work harder to push you out of the dent your foot made in the sand to move you forward. While more of a struggle than running on other terrain, it can help you get in better shape more quickly. If you need convincing that sand will get you fit, consider the fact that Steve Ovett, Britain's former Olympic track champion, did much of his training on Merthyr Mawr sand dunes near Bridgend, some 20 miles west of Cardiff along the M4. The dunes and beach there stretch for miles and are well worth a trip if you are seeking sand-satisfaction in the UK.

HOW TO DO IT

If you can, avoid the shore's slope, which can cause strain in the knees, calves and ankles, and run on damp, more solid sand near the water line. If you have no choice but to hit the soft stuff, experts suggest shortening your stride for a more even-footed landing and keeping your weight balanced to avoid sinking in. And when you get too hot and sweaty, just head for the water. Even at ankle depth, the water provides resistance, which will test your muscles far more than on land. Wade in at waist level and you could burn 270 calories in half an hour.

EQUIPMENT

Many specialists encourage runners to wear trainers for safety and to protect their feet from rocks and shells. But experienced beach runners often prefer to ditch their shoes and run barefoot instead (see page 80).

BODY BOOSTING

■ **Muscles –** A Turkish study of 60 men aged 15 to 21 showed that beach running produced a greater increase in calf circumference over road running as well as a larger boost in maximum aerobic power (VO2 max). The calf size increases came from the muscle overload effect, the researchers found.

■ **Calories** – Belgian researchers concluded that walking on dry sand requires 2.1 to 2.7 times more energy than walking on a hard surface at the same speed. Running on sand requires 1.6 times more energy than does running on a firm surface on which typically you burn 100 calories per mile.

■ **Joints** – A study by Japanese and Australian researchers compared the impact effects of jumping onto sand versus wooden gym floors, concluding that training on sand may carry a lower risk of impact injury than working out on harder surfaces.

RISK FACTOR

Twisted ankles aside, there are few dangers linked to this activity.

COST 

ALSO TRY

Barefoot running/walking – Hold on buying those ultra-cushioned, flashy new trainers. Emerging research into the benefits of barefoot exercise is revealing that it can prevent injuries and even ward off fatigue.

Australian physiotherapists concluded that many people would be better off working out with no trainers than spending a small fortune on the latest high tech shoes. Their groundbreaking study showed that the extra weight of trainers impedes performance far more than a few excess pounds around the midriff. Ease your feet into it gently by walking barefoot on sand (you can also try it on soft, springy grass) before attempting shoe-free workouts lasting no longer than 30 minutes a day. This will allow the thickening of the skin on the sole of the foot and adaptation of the muscles and ligaments. Somewhat ironically, major sports shoe companies are catching on to the concept by developing trainers that precisely mimic the form and movement of the human foot.

Left: Photograph by Don McPhee

* If you can, avoid the shore's slope, which can cause strain in the knees, calves and ankles, and run on the damp, more solid sand near the water line

BODYBOARDING

Once considered the epitome of uncool among surfers, bodyboarding is today one of the most popular water sports on earth. Worldwide sales of bodyboards now exceed three million a year, dwarfing surfboards (250,000) and all other wave-riding devices.

The sport is relatively new, created in 1971 by Hawaiian surfer Tom Morey, who was looking for something new to ride in the waves near his home. Having tried out numerous variations on traditional surfboards, he eventually cut a four-foot block of fibreglass material, softened the edges and hit the swells. The resulting 'Boogie Board' (now a trademarked name) started as a product aimed at surfers' children but Morey soon realised that surfers were buying the boards for themselves. Within four years, he was filling 80,000 orders annually and the sport was firmly established as an alternative to traditional surfing.

HOW TO DO IT

Proponents claim that bodyboarding involves a lot more trickery than surfing. The board is ridden lying down, and because there is no need to stand up and balance, it is much easier to learn and to perform impressive-looking moves. Both the arms and legs can be used to paddle – using the arms requires good balance on the board, positioning yourself so that your nose is a few inches from the top and then practising what is best described as an exaggerated front crawl. As you catch a wave and feel it begin to propel you, stop paddling and shift your weight to the front of the board, using your weight and arms to steer it.

Lessons are advisable – a few basic tips on catching waves will save hours of frustration. Most surfing areas in the UK now have schools offering a range of courses for both surfing and bodyboarding from a two-hour introduction to a week-long course. Join the British Surfing Association (BSA) and you'll get third party public liability insurance as well as discounts on surfing lessons at the BSA's National Surfing Centre and Tolcarne Surf School.

EQUIPMENT

Basic bodyboards today are relatively cheap and portable, made from extruded polystyrene, a high-density Styrofoam, with slick bottoms and veneers of treated foam. They come in different sizes, on average measuring around 42 inches in length. To make sure you get the right sized board, check that the squared off nose is around the same height as your belly button. You will also need a wrist leash or leg rope to prevent you from being separated from your board, a pair of swim fins and ideally a good wetsuit.

BODY BOOSTING

■ **Muscles** – Paddling with the arms will strengthen the biceps, triceps and pectoral (chest) muscles. Using your stomach to help turn the board will also develop core strength and work the lower back muscles.

■ **Calories** – Expect to burn about 300 an hour, more if you spend most of your time paddling and doing tricks.

RISK FACTOR

There have been numerous high profile accidents among bodyboarders in recent years as this relatively new sport has become more popular. Inexperienced bodyboarders can fall prey to rip tides – strong currents of water that carry swimmers out to sea. Bodyboards are usually attached to the wrist by a leash, and a common mistake among beginners is to assume that detaching the leash is the first thing to do when they encounter trouble. In fact, experts advise the opposite: the board is a floating object that can be held onto as a safety device in times of danger.

COST   

Bodyboarding is today one of the most popular water sports on earth. Worldwide sales of bodyboards now exceed three million a year

Photography by Tim Travis, downtheroad.org

SAILING

Sailing has always been perceived as a pastime reserved exclusively for the rich and famous, but this image is fast changing. Undoubtedly inspired by the high profile achievements in recent years of British sailors such as Ellen MacArthur, Tracy Edwards, Ben Ainslie and Shirley Robertson, more and more people are testing out their sea legs and taking to the waves. Almost 100,000 people – one third of them women – are members of the Royal Yachting Association (RYA), the governing body of the sport, and around 25,000 people complete beginner courses each year. One of the sport's many attractions is that almost anyone can learn to sail at any age; the RYA attracts just as many people in their 60s and 70s as in their 20s and 30s. There are also courses for children and teenagers.

HOW TO DO IT

By law, anyone can buy a boat and begin sailing from scratch – you need no licence and no qualification – but lessons are certainly advisable, especially for complete beginners. Very few boat hire companies will rent boats to someone who has not completed an RYA course and from a safety point of view it is essential to have some knowledge of how to sail a boat in variable conditions.

There are more than 250 RYA accredited training centres around the UK, offering two main types of courses – one for small boats and one-man dinghies and another for larger boats and yachts. Each requires very different skills, however, basic techniques such as how to gybe, tack and change sails are applicable to all types of sailing. You can then progress through five different levels of tuition from the Start Sailing Level through to the Coastal Skipper and Day Skipper courses as you get more experienced. The top grade is a Yachtmaster qualification in which you learn to use radio communications, forecast weather conditions, sail at night and in dangerous conditions and to skipper a boat. Most introductory courses run either over two weeks or as a residential weekend programme, and you must be able to swim at least 50 metres without stopping to be accepted onto the RYA's basic Start Sailing course.

Learning to sail on holiday, somewhere with reliably balmy weather, is a popular alternative, and the RYA holds details of approved centres where teaching meets required standards.

EQUIPMENT

Since RYA courses and sailing schools supply all the equipment you need to learn, there is relatively little outlay when you first start sailing. All you really need is an appropriate pair of shoes or boots with a slip-proof surface that won't mark the deck. A jacket or wetsuit are good purchases, but most boat owners will be able to equip you for the first few times out on the water. If you really get bitten by the bug, however, you may choose to join a sailing club and then there is the considerable expense of buying a boat to grapple with. In addition, safety equipment such as a lifejacket and radio system are also needed. This is not a cheap sport.

BODY BOOSTING

- **Muscles** – Far from lounging around drinking cosmopolitans on the deck, sailing requires you to be relentlessly on the move, dodging ropes, pulleys and other bodies as you guide the boat. All this activity gives the shoulder, upper back, thigh and chest muscles a good workout. All sailing is good for developing core muscle strength, but in a small boat you work them extra hard as you lean back to pull the sails.
- **Calories** – A day's sailing can be exhausting. Spend six hours pulling, lifting and climbing on deck and you can easily burn up to 1,000 calories – the equivalent of jogging for more than 90 minutes. Most top sailors have a very high strength to weight ratio, which means they are immensely strong, but carry very little body fat.

RISK FACTOR

Sailing is not without its dangers, and all beginners who learn with an approved instructor must undergo basic safety training before even getting in a boat. You will need the basics of first aid, emergency communications and what to do in a 'man overboard' or capsize situation.

COST    £

Both photographs by Tom Jenkins

E22
GBR 87
GBR 30
GBR 65
GBR 98
GBR 77
GBR 49
GBR131
GBR 117
GBR118
GBR 90
GBR 86
GBR59
GBR 16

FISHING

There are three main types of fishing in the UK – coarse fishing (on rivers and lakes for 'ciprinid' fish such as roach, bream or carp which are always put back); game fishing (for 'salmonid' fish, using artificially tied flies) and sea fishing (in coastal waters for sea fish). Combined, they make it the most active participation sport in the country with an estimated 3.9 million people (that's nine per cent of the population) taking part per year. To keen fishermen, the beauty of the sport is its process and not the fact that it is a means to an end. In fact, conservation concerns mean that more fish than ever are now put back into the water whilst still alive – even 55 per cent of salmon are replaced.

HOW TO DO IT

Angling methods vary according to the type of fish you are catching and the weather conditions on the day. A downside of fishing is that while warm, sunny weather is the most appealing time to take to the water, you are less likely to catch anything when the sun is out. Fish get sluggish in hot weather, staying away from bait. The best conditions are actually warm and overcast with a slight wind.

Most people start out with coarse fishing (in which a float is held in place by 'shots' or weights that can be altered in position to vary the depth at which the bait is presented to the fish) or pole fishing (which involves no reel and uses a telescopic fishing pole instead). Still water with no current is the easiest place to make your first fishing forays. It is considered relatively easy to learn coarse fishing, and children are often introduced to the sport by tying bread or maggots onto the end of a line. Sea fishing is also easier to learn than game fishing, although less accessible for many people.

Accompanying an experienced fisherman is a good introduction, or alternatively, the Salmon and Trout Association runs beginner courses for all age groups, and stages more than 100 courses nationwide every year.

Left: Photograph by David Sillitoe Right: Image courtesy of the Countryside Alliance

* To keen fishermen, the beauty of the sport is its process and not the fact that it is a means to an end

Image courtesy of the Countryside Alliance

EQUIPMENT

Any angler over the age of 12 who is fishing for salmon, trout, freshwater fish or eels in England and Wales needs an Agency Rod Licence which can be purchased online, at a post office or by contacting the Environment Agency directly. They are available for adults and juniors as a one-day, eight-day or full season licences, and the revenue they bring in is used to fund the Agency's work in managing fisheries. Failure to have a licence can result in a fine of up to £2,500. There is no national rod licence in Scotland and you don't need one for coarse fishing in Ireland. Although these licences are relatively inexpensive (costing only £22-£65 per season), you will also have to pay for any fishery or river that you use, and costs for these can mount up (some charge as much as £250 a day).

On top of that you'll need some basic equipment. Starter kits can be bought inexpensively from most tackle shops. Only as you become more experienced does the range of equipment and technology become slightly more baffling. Start with a 'through action float rod' to provide a smooth curve when playing a fish. Buy the best you can afford – a lightweight, well-balanced rod will make for a much more enjoyable experience. A reel, landing net (in which to put your fish), tackle box, hooks (size 10-14 for beginners) and waterproof footwear with a well-gripped sole are also essential.

BODY BOOSTING

■ **Muscles** – Casting a line engages the shoulder and upper back muscles and is thought to help improve flexibility in the upper body. By squatting and bending, you will also work the gluteal and leg muscles.

■ **Calories** – Walking to the venue with your gear burns more calories per hour than fishing, which will use only about 135 as you sit and wait for a bite.

■ **Mind** - Fishing is more akin to yoga than trail running, its benefits being a meditative calm and inner focus.

RISK FACTOR

As with any activity that focuses on one side of the body more than the other (as fishermen do when casting), there is a risk of muscle imbalance, which can lead to back pain. If you fish regularly it is advisable to compensate by performing arm-strengthening exercises for the less-dominant side of your body.

COST   

CASTING FOR RECOVERY

Fishing offers proven benefits for recovering breast cancer patients – the casting action provides the gentle exercise recommended by physiotherapists for joint and soft tissue mobility. As such, the Casting for Recovery charity, which was founded ten years ago in the United States, has helped more than 2,000 breast cancer survivors to date by providing them with free fly fishing retreats. Recently launched in the UK, the charity has joined forces with the England Ladies Fly-fishing Association and the Countryside Alliance to offer free-of-charge weekend retreats to any breast cancer survivor who has medical clearance from their doctor. Trained medical staff and fly-fishing instructors are on hand at all times.

Image courtesy of Casting for Recovery

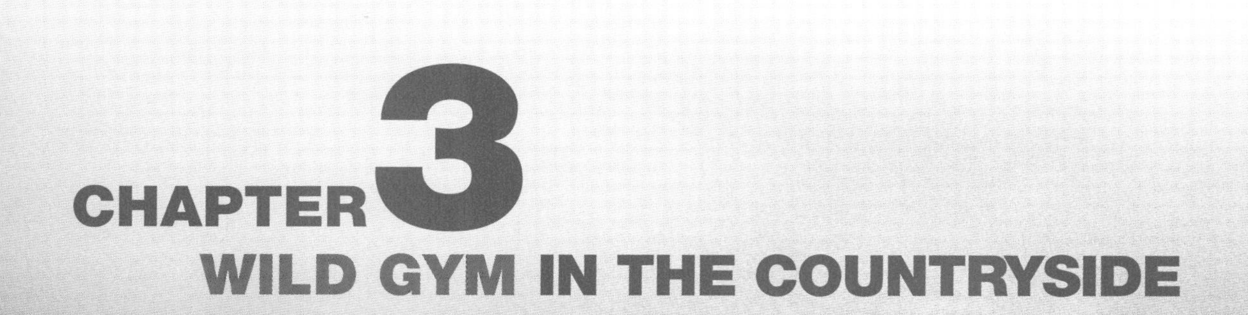

CHAPTER 3
WILD GYM IN THE COUNTRYSIDE

Photograph by Don McPhee

rambles you are likely to use the upper body more, particularly the core muscles, which are engaged over rocky and bumpy ground in an effort to keep you balanced.

■ **Calories** – The more tricky the terrain, the greater the number of calories you will burn. On a hilly route in windy weather (the resistance of wind makes you work harder), you can expect to use between 480 and 510 per hour.

■ **Heart** – Visit your GP and you will soon find yourself prescribed a ramble to improve your health. In conjunction with the British Heart Foundation, the Department of Health is currently trialling a scheme of 'health walks', with findings to be submitted to the National Institute for Clinical Excellence. If the scheme proves effective, it could lead to a network of rambling groups being set up and paid for by the NHS.

■ **Cholesterol** – A study of hikers in the Alps found that different types of walking had different effects on fats and sugars in the blood. Going uphill cleared fats from the blood faster, walking downhill reduced blood sugar more, and hiking either way lowered bad cholesterol.

■ **Blood pressure** – Just three long walks a week can reduce waist and hip circumference and lower blood pressure according to one study. Other researchers looked at the effects of walking on stony ground and found subjects who did so for 16 weeks showed marked improvement in blood pressure and balance.

RISK FACTOR

Twisted ankles are a risk, which is why supportive boots are important. It is also wise to take basic safety precautions if you are heading to isolated areas or walking alone. Tell people where you are going, carry some food and drink in a rucksack as well as extra layers (including a waterproof) should the weather change suddenly, and always take a mobile phone for emergencies.

COST  

LOOKING FOR LOVE?

Lonely hearts should book their trip to the Isle of Wight walking festival in the spring. This 16-day event, which attracts 15,500 participants, is the biggest of its kind in the UK. There are challenges to each of the 180 walks (covering a total of 72,000 miles) but none quite like the speed dating walk. Potential lovebirds meet at a local pub before heading off on a three-hour coastal hike, swapping partners at five-minute intervals. At the finish, they are advised of any matches while tending to their blistered feet.

Photograph by Denis Thorpe

TRAIL RUNNING

The concept of 'trail running' first emerged onto the fitness scene in the 1990s. There are numerous theories as to where the term came from, but the most likely is that this was a rebranding venture initiated by sports shoe manufacturers to make the concept of cross country (so often associated with cold and unpleasant compulsory PE lessons) more fashionable, in order to market new products. Certainly, it has captured the imagination of thousands of people. Initially billed as non-competitive, there are now hundreds of trail running races held every week as well as clubs you can join to follow trails with fellow enthusiasts.

HOW TO DO IT

By definition you can trail run anywhere that isn't a road – so towpaths, parkland, footpaths, beaches, forests and woods are all ideal venues. Technique is much the same as other forms of running, although you should aim to take short, quick steps so you can react to any sudden undulations or obstacles – a stride rate of about 90 steps per minute is recommended. To enthusiasts its greatest appeal is its unpredictability – the ultimate trail run is one previously unexplored and performed with the help of a map to pick out the appropriate route. Remember that covering hills and muddy ground is tougher than running on a flat surface, so make sure you set your goal by time rather than distance. As a guideline, experienced trail runners cover about six miles an hour and less fit runners should aim for four.

You can also take part in trail races, which are now held around the country. In these you will follow a pre-marked route much the same as you would in a traditional cross-country event. If you do decide to take off-road running to another level, then it is wise to join a running or athletics club where free coaching and a social structure will introduce you to the variety of trail-running activities and tracks around your area. You will also find out more about hill-training, interval running and fartlek (a Swedish term meaning 'speed play' used as a training method to vary running speeds), all important in developing speed and stamina for this sport.

Trail camps offer holiday opportunities for those looking either to get faster and fitter or to simply enjoy running in scenic and stimulating environments. It is wise to check the credentials of those who stage them before you book. For expert guidance, coaches should have recognised qualifications and preferably be registered with UK Athletics.

EQUIPMENT

All the big sportswear companies, and a number of outdoor specialists, now make off-road shoes. While each has its individual appeal, the key features are broadly similar – they have rugged, heavily studded outsoles for grip, and tough, durable uppers to cope with the rocks, roots and general debris. Better-cushioned shoes are designed for well-maintained paths and occasional forays on tarmac. The more difficult or extreme the terrain, the more grip you need.

Investing in an ordnance survey map is a good way to investigate what is on offer near your home – you may be surprised.

BODY BOOSTING

- **Muscles** – Muscles in the lower leg have to work harder to keep the body balanced and upright when running off-road.
- **Calories** – Studies comparing road running to running on rough terrains showed that the latter required 26 per cent more energy which means you can burn around 122 calories per mile at a reasonable pace.

RISK FACTOR

Even experienced trail runners can get into trouble on unpredictable and isolated terrain. On a new trail, go with someone who knows it well and take a map, compass, mobile phone and whistle to attract attention. At higher elevations, temperatures can change and storms can roll in quickly, so plan accordingly.

COST 

ALSO TRY

The Pose Method – For 30 years Dr Nicholas Romanov, a Russian sports scientist, has been fine-tuning an approach he calls the 'Pose' method. Romanov, who was recruited by the British Triathlon Association after the Sydney Olympics, believes most runners – including top athletes – need to un-learn their running styles and to reprogramme their bodies to move in an entirely different way. Inefficient technique slows people down and leaves them vulnerable to niggles and strains. Romanov addresses these problems using video analysis and training aids such as rubber ropes that strap around the ankles and are held by a partner who applies resistance as an athlete attempts to run landing 'only on the balls of the feet', not the heels, with 'legs moving directly beneath the torso'.

Left: Image courtesy of Pose Method, posetech.com Right: Photograph by Pete Hartley, lakelandtrials.org

699
590

RETRO WALKING/RUNNING

Most people feel at times that their fitness regimens are heading in reverse, but never quite to the extent they might with retro walking. Walking or running backwards – retro style as it is known among enthusiasts – has few obvious attractions to the casual observer, yet an increasing number of people who try it claim it quite literally gives their exercise programme a whole new perspective. Retro-running dates back to the 1970s when a small group of physiotherapists began recommending it to injured athletes. Now top athletes – including footballers, rugby players and referees – use it as part of their training. Champion boxer, Gene Tunney, ran between four and eight miles a day backwards and Muhammad Ali incorporated backward motion into his daily workouts. There are even backward running races held across Europe and America – top retro runner Timothy Badyna, known as Backwards Bud, backpeddled his way through a full 26.2 mile marathon in under four hours.

HOW TO DO IT

Aside from the fact that you are going to attract some bemused glances should you step backwards out of your front door and proceed to retro run down the local high street, there is the significant drawback of a lack of hindsight. Go slowly, taking small steps at first, and stay in control. Let the ball of the foot contact first, then allow the heel to touch just briefly. If this feels okay, repeat the one-minute segments two or three times, jogging forwards slowly in-between. After a few weeks you should feel less anxious about collisions and can begin to step up your retro running to five or six minutes in total. Try taking longer steps and, if you want to stretch your legs more, try running backwards on a slightly downhill slope.

EQUIPMENT

A good pair of running or walking shoes and layers of lightweight, sweat absorbent clothing are all that is needed to get started.

BODY BOOSTING

■ **Muscles** – Retro running basically uses the same muscles as regular running or walking, although the hamstrings (at the back of the thigh) tend to work harder than the quadriceps (at the front), as do the calf muscles, which can become a little tight if you run too far backwards at your first attempt.

■ **Calories** – Inspiringly, proponents say it burns one fifth more calories than regular walking or running which means you can expect to use around 110-115 per mile covered.

■ **Cardiovascular** – One study found backward training improved cardiorespiratory fitness while

Go slowly, taking small steps at first, and stay in control

helping to streamline the physique of a group of novice runners. Researchers looked at the effects of a six-week, thrice weekly backward running programme on female students compared with a group who stuck to their regular activity schedule. At the end of the study, the retro-runners were found to have significant decreases in oxygen consumption, meaning they had become aerobically fitter, and had lost an average 2.5 per cent of their body fat.

■ **Other** – There is less movement of the hips running this way which means the impact on the joints decreases, making it an ideal activity for people recovering from knee and back problems. Your balance, hearing and peripheral vision will also improve.

RISK FACTOR

Not surprisingly, you run a high risk of bumping into things – lampposts, parked cars, roadsigns or pedestrians – if you head off in reverse in a busy area. For this reason, the activity is best suited for rural, open spaces. Start somewhere safe such as a track, path or field where you will avoid such hazards. Many beginners complain of stiff neck muscles when they first take up retro running as they strain to look behind them in a bid to avoid collisions.

COST 

HORSE RIDING

Britain has a long-standing love affair with horse riding. From childhoods spent taking lessons and mucking out at the local stables through to disabled riding centres and equestrian glory at Olympic level, the sport has broad appeal and is one that has maintained its popularity over the years. According to the British Equestrian Trade Association, the number of people who regularly take to horseback now exceeds 2.5 million with 70 per cent of regulars being women. Not many own their own horse, preferring instead to make use of those at local stables and riding schools.

Despite its popularity, horse riding in Britain is not without its problems, and the grass roots structure of riding is under threat from the growing compensation culture. Dozens of schools are being forced to close because of crippling insurance premiums and customer claims. The British Horse Society (BHS), a charity that approves many of the country's equestrian centres, says the number of schools on its lists has dropped to 700 from 774 in 1993, and the Association of British Riding Schools (ABRS) estimates a 30 per cent decline in numbers since 1988 with a current total of around 2,000.

HOW TO DO IT

You are never too old to take up riding and, if you have lessons, learning the basics is relatively straightforward. At schools approved by the BHS, where instructors, equipment and horses are regularly assessed to ensure they meet stringent standards, group or individual lessons that include the loan of a riding hat are relatively inexpensive. Many schools also offer reductions for booking six lessons or more.

Rhythm and good posture are the most important things to focus on. In beginner lessons, the instruction is usually to imagine a plumb line running from ear to shoulder and from hip to heel as you sit on the horse. Open the hips, allow the lower legs to drop and push the weight down to your heels to stay balanced – the slightest shift in position, such as leaning too far forward or gripping too hard with the knees, can unbalance the horse, so remaining ramrod straight in the back is paramount.

EQUIPMENT

Investing in equipment is not necessary until you have decided the sport is for you. Riding in jeans is inadvisable as the seams are likely to rub your inner thighs. Similarly, you must not ride in trainers or other flat shoes, as the lack of a heel means your

Main photograph by Denis Thorpe

foot can easily slip through the stirrup, leaving you suspended upside down should you come out of the saddle. To start out, you'll need well-fitting, comfortable trousers, a hat, and sturdy shoes or boots with a small heel and you'll be all set for action.

BODY BOOSTING

■ **Muscles** – Riding will strengthen and tone the buttock, thigh and leg muscles without necessarily adding bulk. The adductor muscles on the inside of the thigh work the hardest because they are used to grip the horse, but you will also rely on the pelvic and back muscles as you try to control speed and change direction.

■ **Calories** – Riding's reputation as a sport for the lazy is something of an exaggerated myth. As a means of getting fit, it doesn't offer much in the way of calorie burning (about 150-170 per hour). However, it does require concentration and is a great way to tone the entire body. Also, the peripheral activities can be more arduous – mucking out is an excellent way to burn calories (about 340 an hour).

■ **Mind** – Improved self-confidence comes with knowing that you are exerting control over a half-ton horse and as a stress-buster, riding is second to none.

RISK FACTOR

Horses stand at approximately three metres high and can reach speeds of 30 mph, so there is inevitably a risk of falling off and in inexperienced hands a horse can be lethal. Riding injuries were made infamous when the actor who played Superman, Christopher Reeve, a gifted horseman, was left paralysed after a riding accident. One American study showed falls account for 45 per cent of riding injuries, with injury from being kicked following at 35 percent. The good news is that none of the patients who had worn helmets suffered fractures, the most serious type of riding injury. Despite these risks, riding remains a statistically safer sport to play than rugby and other contact sports and is not nearly so dangerous as some insurance companies like to make out.

COST   

Photograph by Don McPhee

HIPPOTHERAPY

Horse riding as a therapy – called hippotherapy – is used to help people of all ages with physical or psychological difficulties ranging from cerebral palsy, spina bifida and multiple sclerosis to trauma and neurological problems. The treatment involves putting patients on horseback in a variety of positions and letting them adapt to the horse's movements, working with them on coordination and posture. Because the temperature of the horse is about 38 degrees, higher than that of a human, it is relaxing and the warmth is thought to increase blood supply to release tight tissues. Sitting up astride a horse increases the base area of support for the patient's pelvic area, and the movement of riding stimulates postural responses similar to the pattern of walking.

GARDENING

Research has shown that pruning, weeding and tending to your flower beds can help to rid the body of tension in the same way as yoga. In a three-year study conducted with the therapeutic horticultural society, Thrive, researchers at Loughborough University found that gardening had a positive effect on the physical and emotional health of people with stress, depression or other mental health problems. Those who led the research found that gardeners had more time for self-reflection and relaxation, boosting their mood.

HOW TO DO IT

Of course, if you have your own garden, you need only step into it and get to work. However, a scheme called Green Gym, run by the British Trust for Conservation Volunteers, offers those with less access a way of keeping fit in the open air by engaging in everything from clearing woodland and building dry stone walls to repairing footpaths. Supported by the Department of Health, who work in partnership with relevant primary-care trust and local authorities in a particular area, these Green Gyms operate in most parts of the UK, and provide access to a varied and meaningful form of exercise to people who may be averse to traditional ways of working out. Doctors and other organisations refer people to them for help with weight loss or recuperation from illness and injury. If you start, you are more than likely to keep it up. A study of Green Gym participants found that 70 per cent were still at it six months after starting.

Main photograph by Sean Smith

EQUIPMENT

Can all be found in your garden shed. At Green Gyms, all necessary equipment is provided.

BODY BOOSTING

■ **Muscles** – Research carried out at Oxford Brookes University found that regular Green Gym sessions improved cardiovascular fitness and muscular strength by allowing people to work at an activity and pace that suits them.

■ **Calories** – Felling or planting trees, or just plain digging, burns as many calories an hour as step aerobics (around 400).

■ **Mind** – Thrive and the Mental Health Foundation are looking into the benefits of social and therapeutic horticulture for those with depression. Over 24,000 people a week use gardening projects to benefit their health, and research by Thrive shows that many of those claim it helps to boost their mood quite significantly. Similarly, studies by the

Photograph by Tina Stallard, courtesy of Natural England

Gardening had a positive effect on the physical and emotional health of people with stress and depression

American Horticulture Therapy Association have shown a link between ADHD and insufficient time in gardens. They also showed that older people with physical or even memory problems appeared to benefit from community gardening programmes. Several researchers have theorised that bacteria in soil might trigger the release of seretonin, a chemical produced by the brain that lifts the spirits.

RISK FACTOR

Backache is a notorious side effect of gardening and it is essential to practise good technique whenever bending or twisting as you stoop to weed, plant or dig. Always stretch before and after you take to the garden and relax in a warm bath when you finish.

COST  £

ALSO TRY

Tree climbing – One of the things the Playstation Generation misses out on is the exhilarating childhood activity of climbing trees. Statistics by the Royal Society for the Prevention of Accidents has shown that children today are more likely to suffer injuries brought on by playing at the computer than from falling out of a tree's branches. Numbers of those admitted to hospital as a result of injuries incurred from falling from a tree dropped from 1999 to 2006 by 36 per cent. However, something of a resurgence in the popularity of tree climbing is gripping adults around the country who see it as the latest adventure sport. Unlike the free climbing, which most of them did as children, the new trend is to climb much bigger trees in safety. Tree-climbing courses are now running around the UK where you can learn how to ascend and descend via a maze of branches using ropes, harnesses and climbs of up to 20 metres. Contrary to what you might think, climbing trees requires stronger legs than arms as it's the legs that are used to drive the body up to the top branches. However, with this new approach to climbing, technique becomes more important than physical strength. Additions to gear will appear as you gain experience, including mechanical ascenders and special ropes.

Photograph by Paul McCathie, Goodleaf Tree Climbing

KITE FLYING

Far from belonging in children's toy shops, kites have enormous cultural significance. They have been around for nearly 3,000 years and have been used over the centuries for everything from religious occasions to meteorological studies to signalling purposes and even for pulling vehicles. Today though, kites are primarily used for recreation, and a huge spectrum of kites are on offer, from power kites, to stunt kites, to kites that, in conjunction with engineered skateboards, surfboards and buggies, provide access to a whole new range of adventure sports. The sense of liberation experienced by harnessing wind power in this way can be exhilarating and soul-soothing in equal measure.

HOW TO DO IT

Experienced kite flyers say that, while some wind is essential, a light breeze (5-25 mph) rather than strong gust is ideal, and that conditions should not be too sunny (a bright sun can blind you as you look upwards). To begin, stand with your back to the wind and hold your kite up by the bridle point to let the line out. If there is enough wind, your kite will go right up. Allow it to fly away from you a little, then pull in on the line as the kite points upwards so it continues to climb. Repeat this until your kite reaches a good steady wind. If the kite sinks tail first, there might not be enough wind; if it comes down head first or spins, it could be too windy.

EQUIPMENT

For beginners, the best kites to start with are simple delta or diamond shapes, which can fly in much lighter winds than other shapes and can lift and dive on very weak rising pockets of air or thermals. Once you become proficient, you can progress to either a simple stunt kite or a parafoil kite. The former is flown with two strings, one held in each hand, so that the kite can be made to loop and dive at high speeds, depending on wind conditions. Parafoil kites can be controlled with one line or two and have vented cells that fill with air, making them powerful, stable and virtually indestructible. Other types of kites include box kites, which are known for their

Photograph by Tina Stallard, courtesy of Natural England

The sense of liberation experienced by harnessing wind power in this way can be exhilarating and soul-soothing in equal measure

power and stability in strong, steady winds and dragon kites, which appear to 'swim' through the air and range in length from 25 to 55 feet. Multi-line stunt kites – also known as sport kites – are generally used in the kite-flying competitions that are held all over the UK and internationally. They allow for much greater artistic movement and are often flown in teams with up to eight pilots stacking kites within inches of each other to dramatic effect. Their power means that greater control is needed and many sports kite fliers wear knee and elbow pads to prevent injuries should they fall.

BODY BOOSTING

- **Muscles** – The extent to which muscles are used depends on the size of your kite and the wind resistance it creates. The arm and shoulder muscles are used to hold the kite in position, but much of the power comes from the legs, especially the thigh muscles, which are engaged to keep the kite-flier grounded.
- **Calories** – You can burn anywhere between 180 and 320 calories an hour flying a kite. The bigger and more powerful the kite, the more calories you will burn.
- **Mind** – The mental health charity, MIND, cites kite-flying as among the best means to alleviating mild to moderate depression and stress. In studies it found that as many as 71 per cent of mild to moderately depressed people experienced significant improvements in their mood after kite-flying sessions.

RISK FACTOR

Kites are classified as aircraft according to Civil Aviation legislation and there are various basic safety rules to consider. Never fly kites in wet or stormy weather as static electricity can build up and be conducted down the line. This is also the reason why you should never fly a kite with wire or anything metallic in the line. If you are new to kite flying make sure there is plenty of room around you – kites can be dangerous if they are flown in the way of pedestrians or other bystanders, and can distract drivers if flown too close to roads.

COST  

ALSO TRY

Kitesurfing – If kite flying does not provide the kind of adrenaline rush you seek from an afternoon outside, then you might want to try this variation on the activity. Kitesurfing (also known as kiteboarding) is among the fastest growing adrenaline activities in the UK. Using a wakeboard and a kite to harness wind power, experienced kitesurfers can reach speeds of 20 metres per second in the water and jump up to ten metres in the air. A one day course will teach you the basics and introduce you gently to the exhilarating effects as the kite 'body drags' you across the water.

LANDYACHTING

Imagine you are spending a day on a yacht. Do you see yourself relaxing on the deck of a gleaming white vessel under clear blue Mediterranean skies, or do you see yourself deep in the Cambridge countryside on a bumpy, disused runway? If you lack the requisite boat (or ocean), then this is just one area in the rural UK that you can try landyachting. A basic landyacht has three wheels (one at the front and two at the back), a large sail and two pedals in the body of the yacht to enable you to steer. Think windsurfer on wheels and you get the picture. With funding from Sport England, the British are highly successful at this world-wide recognised sport, and landyachters have brought home medals from almost every major international championship in recent years. Age is not a barrier in this sport – people in their 70s have represented the British landyachting team.

HOW TO DO IT

Landyachting relies on blustery winds – it is not safe to sail in particularly foul weather conditions such as fog or snow, but a perfectly calm day doesn't suit either. Sitting in the body of the wheeled vessel, strapped in with a seatbelt, the idea is to hold onto a rope connected to the sail. Just enough pressure should be applied to the pedals to manoeuvre the vessel, and pulling or easing the rope will also help you steer. A level one landyachting certificate can be completed as part of a one-day course; complete levels 2 and 3 and you can apply for a pilot's racing licence. Most enthusiasts join clubs affiliated to the British Federation of Sand and Land Yacht Clubs, which provides insurance, training days and details of how to enter competitions. There are around 15 clubs in England and several in Scotland and Wales.

EQUIPMENT

Most schools will provide the equipment you need, but you will be asked to wear skiwear or thick clothing in cold weather (it gets nippy out there), thick gloves and a pair of old trainers. Helmets are compulsory. Racing landyachts are highly technical in design with top notch models being constructed mainly from fibreglass with axles made from ash. Some are adapted for use on sand and the best enable you to hit speeds of 95 mph.

BODY BOOSTING

■ **Muscles** – All the pulling on the rope to change direction works the arm and shoulder muscles. You also use your leg muscles and regularly engage the core muscles as you turn and slow down the yacht.
■ **Calories** – You will burn about 220 calories an hour – more if you are working into a particularly strong headwind.

Photograph by Rob Collins, Anglia Land Yacht Club

RISK FACTOR

Like most wind-powered wheel machines, landyachts do not have a brake and are slowed down by heading directly into the wind. For this reason, accidents do happen, especially around pedestrians, which is why lessons are crucial in order to learn safety procedures and good technique.

COST

£ £ £ £ £

GERRARD
4

GOLF

Golf, once handicapped by a rather fusty image of men with money, has undergone a dramatic makeover and is now attracting a younger, more hip generation of players. Even A-list celebrities are venturing onto the fairway. Catherine Zeta-Jones, Michael Douglas, Hugh Grant, Sylvester Stallone and Jodie Kidd are among those who swing their clubs regularly. Undoubtedly its attraction is that, unlike other sports, the biggest opponents are oneself and the surroundings. Even at professional level, golfers claim to battle the course as much as their rivals.

At club level, golf in the UK has tried hard to shake of its sexist image but changes have been slow. The private status of clubs provides a legal loophole enabling them to resist progress made by other sports, such as tennis, football and athletics, and women in many parts of the Britain still struggle to get through the front door of their local clubhouse. The sport's reputation as male dominated is undoubtedly exacerbating the lack of interest among schoolgirls; 91 per cent of the 60,000 junior golfers registered in England are boys and the average number of girl members per club is only seven.

HOW TO DO IT

The basics of the game are simple: hit a small ball into a hole with the fewest possible shots. Repeat 18 times (shorter nine hole courses are also common). The first shot on each hole is played from an area called a tee, beyond which is a combination of long grass (called rough) and manicured lawn (known as the fairway) leading to the green where the target hole is marked by a yellow or red flag.

Bunkers, streams and other hazards are positioned on a course to add to the variety. As you play, the idea is to count the number of shots taken plus any penalties you may incur. A scoring system – called the par – is calculated based on the number of shots it takes a professional to complete a course, usually between 70 and 72. Each hole has a par according to its length and difficulty. So, for example, a par-three hole lets you have three shots. If you take 100 shots to go around a course and your opponent takes 104, you win. However, the handicapping system in golf allows you to play against better players by giving you extra shots, akin to a head start.

Booking lessons is highly recommended, as good technique will really help you enjoy the game. Developing rotation and range of movement in the spine and hips is the key to perfecting your swing. Golf clubs (where you can be taught by a pro) are currently in a drive to recruit members, especially women after membership figures dropped

Photograph by Dan Chung

substantially in recent years. They can be pricey, but many offer special deals and pay-as-you-go trials, so shop around. For a cheaper option, contact your local authority for details of what's on offer at the local municipal course. Schemes such as Tri-Golf, in which children are introduced to the game using large plastic clubs, are definitely helping to raise the profile among younger age groups. A joint campaign by the English Ladies' Golf Association and the English Golf Union, called Get Into Golf, offers free coaching to newcomers of all ages.

EQUIPMENT

Golfers are allowed a maximum of 14 clubs in their bags. There are three main categories of clubs – woods, irons and putters – each designed to cope with particular conditions or terrain. Woods (so-called because they were traditionally made of wood) have big bulky heads, and are traditionally used for long shots – so ideal for teeing off. Irons are used for shorter shots and are usually numbered from two to nine according to the angle of their face (the lower the number, the steeper the angle and the further the ball is likely to be hit). A putter has minimal loft, and is used to put the ball into the hole. Pitching wedges and sand irons (to be used from a bunker) can also be used to negotiate the course's hazards.

BODY BOOSTING

■ **Muscles** – Not so much a good walk spoiled, as Mark Twain famously described it, but a good walk enhanced by the technical demands of the game and of

Photograph by Tom Jenkins

* Golf, once handicapped by a rather fusty image of men with money, has undergone a dramatic makeover and is now attracting a younger, more hip generation of players

carrying a hefty bag (weighing up to 15kg) as you cover the fairway. Through the swing, golf develops good core stability and back strength and the two hours plus of walking will help to keep you aerobically fit.

■ **Calories** – Most courses are around 6,000 yards long and take between three to four hours to play 18 holes. During this time, you will probably end up walking about five miles, and you'll burn between 250-320 calories an hour.

RISK FACTOR

As numbers of newcomers to golf rise, so too does the tally of injuries they suffer as a consequence of poor technique, researchers at the Union Memorial Hospital in Baltimore found. Among the most common problems are damage to the lower back caused by the twist of swinging, tennis elbow and shoulder damage. Most amateur players will swing the club up to 150 times in a single round of golf. During an average swing, the rotation of the spine can reach speeds of 500 degrees a second. Without proper spinal conditioning, this constant wear and tear can cause damage to the lower back. Always perform a thorough warm up of walking followed by mobility exercises using a club. For instance, stand feet apart with the club positioned on your shoulders and twist from side to side. Physiotherapists recommend that any golfing programme be complemented by pilates-style exercises to strengthen core muscles (which support the back).

COST £ £ £ £ £

Photograph by Dan Chung

GOLF JARGON

Albatross: Three shots less than par
Eagle: Two shots less
Birdie: One shot less
Bogey: One shot more
Double bogey: Two shots more
Triple bogey: Three shots
Chip: A short shot with a short swing normally played to the green with a lofted club. The hands do not pass hip height and the wrists hinge very little
Driver: One wood, the longest club in the bag, used for hitting from the tee.
Handicap: A calculated number that indicates your level of play. Most people who play golf do not bother to maintain a handicap.

FALCONRY

Falconry is the training of birds of prey to hunt small birds and other animals for humans. Described as the 'sport of kings', this is one of the oldest and most aristocratic of country pastimes. Henry VIII was a keen falconer and reputedly owned 100 albino falcons. However, it took the likes of Madonna and Guy Ritchie to have a go for the ancient sport to take off among the masses. Now falconry schools have been set up around the country and they are regularly full. They often offer access to numerous different types of birds of prey (collectively termed 'raptors') including hawks, falcons, eagles and vultures. Some also keep European eagle owls (a metre tall and with a 2.5 metre wing span), snowy owls and even bald eagles.

It is the sheer exhilaration that comes with interacting with these gracious creatures that is the main pull for many. This sport is not purely about hunting – it requires huge understanding about avian nutrition and health maintenance, and it becomes an art when a falconer knows a bird well enough to figure out how to bring out its best performance.

HOW TO DO IT

Around 4,000 people a year now learn falconry with a British School of Falconry (BSF) instructor based at the Gleneagles Estate in Scotland and many more attend BSF approved courses elsewhere. Day courses offer a taster, although a week-long course is usually enough to ensure comfortable handling of a Harris Hawk. From there you can progress to an afternoon's hawking session in which they hunt for rabbits with the help of ferrets. At most schools you will also learn about the care of the birds – how to feed, manage and fly them in different conditions. Because the birds can be heavy and you need to balance with that weight on your arm, lessons are only usually provided for children aged 12 and upwards.

Raptors can be purchased by anyone in England, without any need to confirm that it will be hunted or even flown. Elsewhere, the number of falconry licences is fixed and the only way to obtain one is when a licence holder relinquishes it or dies. Even if you own a bird, it is a good idea to join a falconry club – you get access to a lot of expert falconers who can pass on tips.

A cautionary note – falconry is time consuming and can gobble up hours of your day should you become hooked.

Both photographs by Dr Matthew Gage

Photograph by Dr Matthew Gage

EQUIPMENT

The leather gloves and Barbour jackets are usually supplied by falconry schools, although it is worth taking your own waterproof clothing along with a good pair of walking shoes or boots (you will be doing this activity in a muddy field). The birds have bells attached to their wings so that they can be detected by their handlers.

BODY BOOSTING

■ **Muscles** – The only muscles engaged in this sport are those in the arms and core – birds of prey can be heavy and you need to be physically strong to handle them.

■ **Calories** – This is not a gut-busting activity, but the concentration, walking and standing around mean you use up to 165 calories an hour.

■ **Mind** – Watching a bird in flight is reputed to have meditative effects on the mind. Confidence is also gained through the knowledge that you are handling some of the fastest creatures on the planet – Peregrine falcons pursue their prey at speeds of up to 100 mph.

RISK FACTOR

Raptors are wild animals and as such can behave unpredictably. They should never be taken for granted, and it is essential to learn to handle them correctly before attempting to go solo.

COST    

DOG SLEDDING

If you thought husky sledding was something that required sub-zero temperatures and was only practised in Sweden, Iceland or the Antarctic, then you will be more than surprised to learn that you can try your hand at it in Bracknell or the Forest of Dean. This activity requires between two and six dogs to be harnessed to a sled (if there is enough snow) or a rig on wheels, and then to pull it (and its passenger/s) along a trail. Since it was introduced in Britain in the 1980s, it has soared in popularity, with regular races of over 10 miles taking place in forests and woods around the UK. When the Siberian Husky Club of Great Britain ran its first meeting at Aviemore in Scotland in 1983 there were just 12 teams taking part. That has risen to almost 250.

HOW TO DO IT

The best way to start is to attend an organised sled dog introductory day where you will be taught the basics of the sport. ABSA (Affiliated British Sleddog Activities) help arrange and run sled dog events around Wales and South England between April and October each year.

The ultimate adrenaline shot comes from racing, but you will need to complete a lot of training before reaching the stage when you can take part in a rally. Sled dog racers are known as 'mushers' within the sport, a term that comes from the traditional call of 'Mush!' used to gee dogs along (these days, 'Mush!' has been replaced by 'Hike On!', but the title remains). It's a fast sport – a wheeled rig can reach speeds of 25 mph – so for those who prefer a more sedate introduction (and time to take in the scenery) opt for a driven sled ride in which a musher will drive a four-wheeled rig with mudguards and suspension for a less bumpy experience.

EQUIPMENT

If you get hooked, the sport can become an expensive way of life. In order to race a single sled you will need a minimum of two dogs that will need a specialist diet, an exercise compound outside your house, running or walking for hours at a time each day and neighbours who won't mind their howling at night. Most race organisations only allow 'pure breed' sled dogs like the Siberian Husky and the Alaskan Malamute to take part. Being the smaller and faster of the breeds, the Siberian Husky is better over shorter distances.

BODY BOOSTING

- **Muscles** – this is harder work than you may think and you will need strong arm, back, leg and abdominal muscles to help steer the dogs and to scoot the sled up slopes and hills.

■ **Calories** – Expect to burn between 300 and 500 calories an hour, depending on the course and the amount of uphill and steering work required.

RISK FACTOR

The risk of falling out of the sled at high speed is the sport's biggest danger. Helmets are usually worn as a precautionary measure.

COST    

ALSO TRY

Cani-cross – If your dog is more prone to taking you for a walk than vice versa, it might be appropriate for the pair of you to take up Cani-Cross. A sport that is growing in popularity, it is endorsed by many pet charities and involves six-legged cross-country races on foot for you and your best friend. Working as a team, you and your pooch complete a route of between two and a half and five kilometres, held in rural and traffic-free environments, throughout which you must remain attached by an ordinary lead. The only rule is that your dog must stay ahead of you at all times. Accessories are available for those pooches who like the idea of pulling their owner along – waist belt leashes (so that your arm doesn't get wrenched out its socket), running harnesses and doggie booties are among those on offer.

Photograph by Tom Jenkins

40

CHAPTER 4
WILD GYM IN THE MOUNTAINS

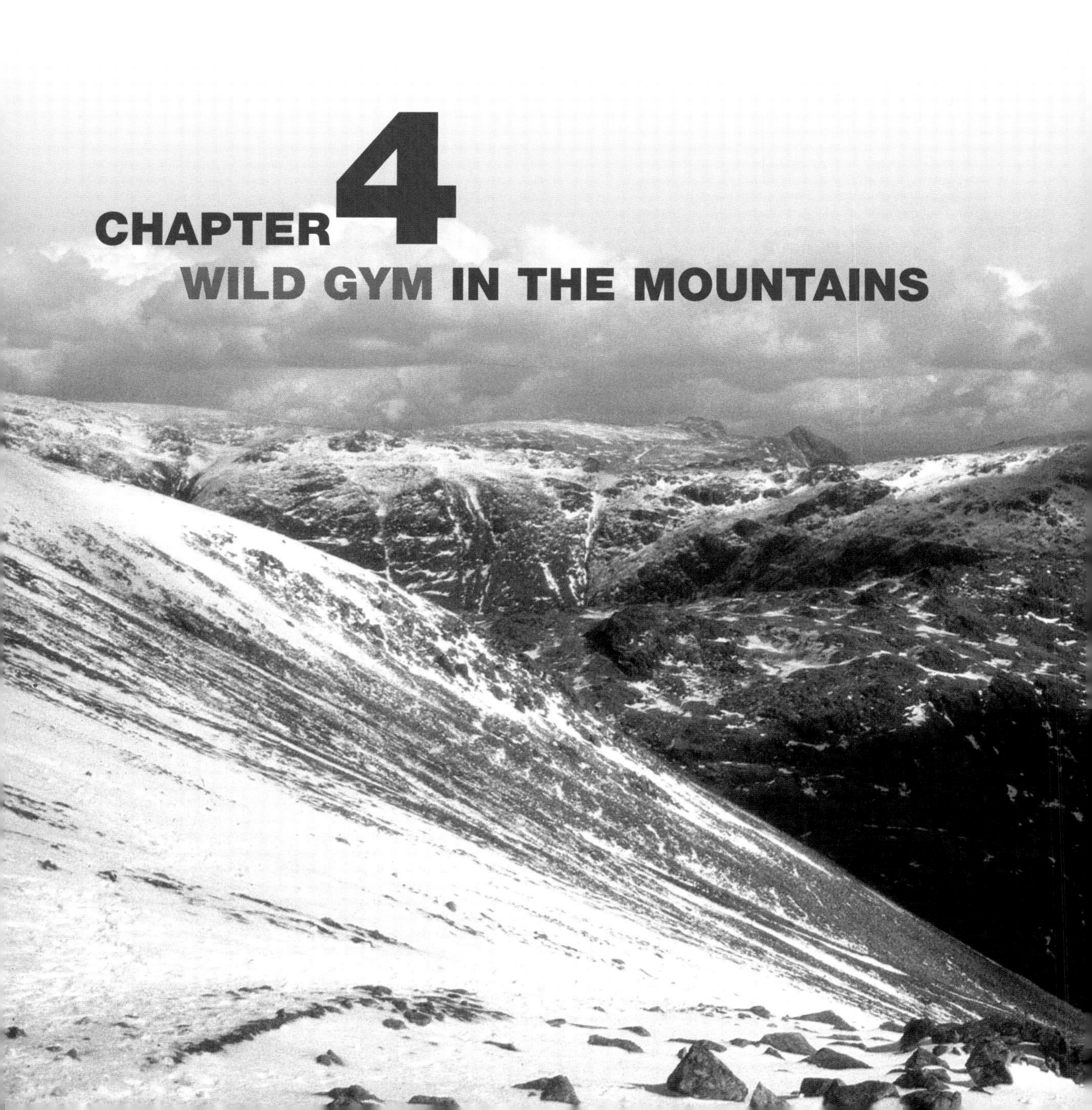

Great things are done
when men and mountains meet
William Blake
Image courtesy of the Countryside Alliance

There is no universally accepted definition of what makes a mountain. In England and Wales, a mountain is a peak over 600 metres in height, whilst in Scotland the term is left open to interpretation. What is certainly true is that mountains mean many different things to different people, and the word can conjure up a multitude of images– a craggy, unassailable, snow-capped peak, perhaps, or a vast green hill criss-crossed with trails. But for most, mountains represent an extreme of nature – a challenge to be either conquered or admired from afar.

Being dramatic and extreme in themselves, mountains tend to attract sports of the same nature. Any activity attempted on a mountain requires colossal amounts of energy, endurance and adrenaline, much more so than on the flat. It also requires careful planning and preparation – weather conditions can change at the drop of a hat, making visibility and safety prime concerns. This is partly the reason that so many mountain activities are performed in groups or pairs, making them ideal for those who like a social element to their sports.

The extreme conditions on mountains can also provide innumerable health benefits. It is no coincidence that many Alpine resorts were traditionally areas of recuperation from diseases such as tuberculosis. Doctors would refer patients to mountain villages such as Leysin in Switzerland in the belief that the fresh air and purity of the surroundings would aid their recovery. Today, doctors continue to advocate the benefits of mountainous surroundings. For example, sufferers of seasonal affective disorder (SAD), a condition that is caused by a lack of sunlight during the winter months and leads to symptoms such as depression and fatigue, are often advised to visit ski resorts where the reflection of sun on snow along with the psychological benefits of being under clear blue skies can help to improve their condition. Top athletes also flock to the mountains, using them as training bases. A lot of European mountain ranges are at altitude, which means that the air is thinner at the top. These reduced oxygen levels create a response in the body called hypoxia, in which it struggles to produce the required energy needed to perform, resulting in an increase in the concentration of red blood cells in the body, and other physiological adaptations that ultimately enhance the efficiency of the respiratory and cardiovascular systems. This makes altitude training ideal for athletes in endurance sports such as long distance running and cycling.

In this chapter we will look at some of the diverse sports and activities you can try on, up, down or even inside any sort of hill or mountain. Do not let the opportunity pass you by: mountains are there to be conquered in any way you choose.

MOUNTAINBOARDING

A mountainboard is essentially a snowboard on wheels or an oversized skateboard complete with a hand held brake. Also called grassboards and all-terrain boards, they were originally developed in 1995 by Austrian snowboarders looking for a way to practise their skills out of season. The idea caught on with keen British snowboarders unable to make it to the piste as often as they liked and with American snowboarders in training for the Winter Olympics, and it was not long before surfers started using them too. Today mountainboarding is a sport in its own right with regional and national leagues being held around the country. A basic model has two wheels at the back and one or two at the front with a deck that is shorter than the average snowboard – approximately 110 cm in length. Many boards manufactured in the UK have foot straps, although the latest models from Austria have bindings similar to snowboards, which enable more experienced boarders to attempt jumps and complicated aerial manouevres.

HOW TO DO IT

Anyone who has tried snowboarding or surfing has a headstart when it comes to learning this sport. It is best to have lessons and to start on a gentle, grassy slope. To turn the board, you must bend your knees and tip your feet forward (right) or backwards (left) while keeping your body upright at all times. Once you get the hang of mountainboarding down a smooth, grassy bank you can progress to something steeper. It is wise to have lessons – often available at hire shops – or to join a mountainboarding group or club where you will get expert advice.

EQUIPMENT

Mountainboards are relatively expensive to buy (around £200 for a basic model), but can be hired as part of a lesson. You need protective shin, knee and wrist pads and a helmet when you are learning, as well as a sturdy pair of boots or trainers and gloves to protect your hands.

BODY BOOSTING

■ **Muscles** – Mountainboarding itself primarily develops leg strength, but dragging the board uphill after every descent is hard work for the arms and upper body.

■ **Calories** – You will burn between 180 and 300 an hour depending on the steepness of the decline.

RISK FACTOR

Beginners tend to be cautious and therefore rarely come back with injuries. However, when confidence levels rise and boarders start to attempt jumps and turns, they are more likely to come a cropper. The ultimate trick, for example, is a double back flip, in which the rider completes two full turns in the air at speeds of 30 mph – and the risks of this going wrong are much more substantial than a straightforward downhill descent.

COST   

ALSO TRY

Rollerskiing – If the concept of snowboarding on grass strikes you as odd, then skiing on wheels will seem equally baffling. Rollerskis, used by cross-country skiers in Scandinavia as a tool for summer training, are basically skis on rubber wheels with ratchets attached to stop you rolling backwards as you skate up steep hills. You even carry ski poles as you glide down hills in parks or on country lanes, down dirt tracks or in empty business parks.

There are two basic techniques to rollerskiing – skating (like inline skating) and classic (more like traditional cross-country skiing in which legs move forwards and backwards as the arms pump). Like its snow-based counterpart, it uses 90 per cent of the body's muscles and is excellent for boosting cardiovascular fitness.

Beginners' courses are available around the UK and there is a growing network of clubs and races.

Photograph by Alistair Brown

ADVENTURE RACING

Take a triathlon, throw in mountains, mud, a kayak, some rocky terrain and the occasional horse and you'll get adventure racing. The first event of this kind was the Raid Gauloises held in France in 1989. In that particular race, which lasted between seven and 10 days, competitors were required to complete a harrowing course involving everything from white water rafting to sky-diving and horse-riding. By the mid 1990s, the trend for these extreme physical challenges had spread to the United States where hundreds of adventure races are held every weekend, and are billed as triathlons with attitude or army assault courses with altitude. Since 1999, when the first series of events was launched in the UK, they have grown in popularity here too.

HOW TO DO IT

What marks these events apart is not just the distance and diversity of challenges faced, but the fact that even at entry level the events usually last between four and six hours. Elite competitions can last several weeks, with racing from dusk until dawn every day. This level of race generally involves some swimming, kayaking or rafting, mountain biking and running. In many, you must enter as a team, usually of three or four and often including an obligatory female member. In most cases, if you don't finish as a team, crossing the line at the same time, you will not even merit an official finishing time.

Entering usually costs a relatively substantial fee compared with, say, running events and it is difficult to take part in any adventure race without having trained for it. Training can be time consuming – experts recommend going swimming three times a week and cycling or running to work (or at lunchtime) if you can. For entry level races you need

Image courtesy of Plas y Brenin, pyb.co.uk

*** Take a triathlon, throw in mountains, mud, a kayak, some rocky terrain and you'll get adventure racing**

to be fit enough to swim half a mile, run three miles and mountain bike 12 miles.

For insurance reasons, most events cater only for the over 18s, however a growing number of youth enthusiasts means that more and more races are becoming available for younger people.

EQUIPMENT

Event organisers will always supply any specialist equipment required, such as buoyancy aids or climbing harnesses. However, you will usually need to bring a compass, a whistle (for emergencies), a day sack (15-20 litre capacity), a bike repair kit, a head torch and spare batteries and a bike helmet. Running shoes of the cross-trainer variety, lightweight trousers and a fleeced and waterproof top should also be taken. It is a good idea to bring some wrap-around sporty sunglasses too – not only will they protect your eyes from the sun but also from leaves and branches when running through forests and from stones thrown up by bike wheels. A wetsuit is often necessary, although they can usually be hired from the organisers on the day of the event.

Joining a triathlon club is the best way to train for and get introduced to adventure racing, as specific clubs for this sport are yet to be formed.

BODY BOOSTING

■ **Muscles** – With such a huge variety of activities, no two adventure races will use the same muscle groups. However, most will engage all of the major muscles in the legs, arms, shoulders, abdominal area and back. It is a true all-round sport.

- **Calories** – Again, the number of calories burned will depend on the specific activities of an event, but you can expect energy expenditure to be high – usually between 400 and 600 an hour.
- **Mind** – These races involve a large amount of planning and tactics, with problem solving often taking place when your energy levels are utterly spent. Unlike triathletes, adventure racers cannot just put their heads down and get on with it.

RISK FACTOR

There have been some highly publicised risks relating to some of the more gruelling, week-long adventure races in far-flung destinations. In one race in Borneo, for example, 25 per cent of participants developed a severe disease, leptospirosis, contracted when they were swimming or kayaking in an infected river. In Europe, safety standards are rigorous, but since most of the disciplines carry an accident risk in themselves, this is a sport that should be prepared for fully and with care.

COST   

ALSO TRY

Extreme ironing - Leicester-based adventure athlete, Phil Shaw, who invented the adrenaline sport of extreme ironing (or ironing under the sky) claims its attraction is that it 'combines the thrill of sport with the satisfaction of a well-pressed shirt'. Quite. Competitors challenge each other to take ironing board and crumpled laundry to the most diverse locations they can find; extreme ironists have pressed their clothes on top of mountains and while abseiling. In 2004, boundaries dictating what can be done with an iron were smashed when 43 scuba divers from Melbourne set a world record for extreme underwater ironing. Sensibly using non-electric irons, they pressed shirts submerged in three metres of sea water on the Bellanine Peninsula. Their record has since been broken.

Both photographs by Rob Howard, TrailPlus

STREETLUGING

Described as downhill Formula 1 without the cars, this is an adrenaline surging sport that, despite its name, usually takes place on off-road mountain trails rather than streets. It was developed after two Californian skateboarders, looking to try something new, lay down on their boards and headed downhill. They discovered that being prostrate gave them greater speed, greater control and a much greater thrill. They then adapted boards by making them longer to accommodate their body lengths, and widening the trucks and the wheels to provide greater stability and speed. Nowadays streetluging (sometimes called landluging) has its own high tech boards and, depending on the gradient and the layout of the track, they can reach speeds of up to 80 mph.

HOW TO DO IT

An advantage is that it is easy to learn – you can be streetluging within a couple of hours. But you do need to be fit to try it. A luger lies on his back, feet pointing downhill, accumulates speed and prays he can make the next corner. Bends are negotiated by leaning with the body and braking with the feet.

Streetluge UK holds taster days for beginners – and almost all the top UK streetluge riders started out this way, including past World Champions Peter Eliot and Jeremy Gilder. Those starting out will be thankful to hear they take to gentle slopes at first, moving relatively sedately at 25 mph, while intermediates get faster at 50 mph. However, as you are a matter of inches off the ground, even at these speeds it feels as though you are going much faster. Luging can be something of a slalom, requiring lightning-fast reflexes as you dodge manholes, trees and other lugers in your path. Although the sport has a competitive element (you can enter races against other streetlugers), much of the appeal is the adrenaline surge it provides. The ultimate goal for many of the top riders is to break a land-speed record.

EQUIPMENT

Learning with a qualified instructor is essential – taking a streetluge out on your own could be highly dangerous if you are inexperienced. Since a luger will inevitably slide off sometimes, protective headgear, gloves and full motorcycle leathers are usually worn and will be provided in lessons.

BODY BOOSTING

- **Muscles** – Because you have to steer the board by leaning, luging recruits the core stability muscles that support your spine. A good level of fitness is required as this sport is tougher than people might imagine.
- **Calories** – Between 220 and 315 an hour.

Image courtesy of Go Fast! Sports

MARUSHIN ★
DAVE
MARUSHIN

RISK FACTOR

Falling off when you are travelling at very high speeds is exceedingly dangerous, hence the requirement of crash helmets and safety equipment. Streetluging lessons usually start off in areas surrounded by grassy verges to make for a softer landing.

COST 

Photograph by Dave Auld

Image courtesy of Downhill Revolution

ALSO TRY

Zorbing – The Zorb, a New Zealand invention, is a gigantic three metre inflatable and transparent ball inside which is another, smaller ball suspended by thousands of nylon threads. The idea is for you and one or two others to squeeze inside the smaller ball, strap yourselves into a harness and get launched off a ramp down a steep track. As the Zorb hurtles downhill, you will flip and tumble inside it. The feeling of weightlessness is second to none in terms of adrenaline rushes, and even though it reaches speeds of 40 mph, the rotational movement makes it strangely therapeutic. To make things more interesting, organisers suggest throwing in a bucket of water.

All the gripping as you try in vain to control the downhill journey will give your stomach and arm muscles a boost, but this is more about the experience than anything else.

SNOWBOARDING

Snowboarding is beginning to rival skiing as the coolest way to descend a slope, and while it hasn't yet overtaken skiing in terms of popularity, around one fifth of the 1.3 million people who head to the slopes each year from the UK now choose boards over skis. It is, according to statistics, the fastest growing snowsport in the world.

HOW TO DO IT

According to instructors, the learning curve for snowboarding is steeper than skiing, which means anyone should be able to grasp the basics within a few days. Beginners will first practise skating (with one foot on the board, one off), and then learn to side-step and turn on flat snow, before progressing to the slopes. You will then learn to slide back and forth across a slope like a 'falling leaf'. This means pressing down with the 'toeside edge' of your front foot to begin sliding, and pulling back up with the same foot to stop. When you reach the edge of the piste, you will slow down and shift your weight to the toes of the other foot, to start sliding in the other direction, creating a falling leaf pattern all the way to the bottom of the run. Tension makes the action harder and more dangerous, so try and stay relaxed at all times. Keep your knees bent a little, and your legs loose to absorb the pressure of any bumps you encounter.

The fact that it is relatively easy to get moving does not mean that snowboarding isn't hard work. Skiers will notice the main difference is that, while you can fall towards the slope on your side when wearing a plank on each foot, on a board you go either forwards (on your wrists, elbows, knees or nose) or backwards (on your bottom, wrists or head), while somersaulting with the board attached means repeatedly pushing yourself up with tired arms.

Snowboarding became an Olympic Sport in 1998 and there are now six snowboard events on the programme of the Winter Games: men's and women's halfpipe (takes place in a half-cylinder-shaped course dug deep into the hill in which acrobatic skills are performed), men's and women's parallel giant slalom (head-to-head downhill races on two side-by-side courses) and the men's and women's snowboard cross (in which boarders cover a challenging route including jumps and obstacles).

EQUIPMENT

All ski resorts provide a huge range of equipment to hire and it is well worth doing this until you decide that boarding is for you. Boards vary according to the snowboarding disciplines – alpine boards with a curved nose and flat tail are designed for speed and tight carving and favoured by slalom riders, freestyle boards are shorter and popular with half-pipe specialists, and free-ride boards are generally the best for beginners as they perform well on most terrain. If you become an advanced snowboarder, you may progress to using an alpine board for more speed. Boots are softer and therefore much more comfortable than those worn for skiing.

Boarding or skiing in sunglasses which don't provide enough protection can cause headaches or, in extreme cases, snow blindness, caused by the cornea being forced to absorb too many UV rays. Choose a pair of lightweight, plastic glasses with 100 per cent UV protection that wrap around the face and won't shatter if you fall. Look for lenses that conform to the EU safety standard.

BODY BOOSTING

■ **Muscles** – Once you have got the hang of it, the snowboarding action actually comes from the stomach, helping you to develop strong abdominal muscles and a flat tum. It is also is particularly good at strengthening the thighs and buttocks, whilst pushing yourself up from the ground develops a strong upper body and arms.

■ **Calories** – The better you become, the more calories you burn, as you will spend less time on the ground, and more time in continuous descent. Beginners burn around 350 calories an hour while more experienced snowboarders can use up to 450.

RISK FACTOR

Fractured wrists are the most common injury – snowboarders are twice as likely to suffer a broken wrist than skiers, because of the way they are forced to fall. The American Council on Exercise research found that 43 per cent of snowboarders who broke their wrists were boarding for the first time. Ankle injuries are also common as a result of less support around the ankles from the soft boots. Boarders are also prone to whiplash-type injuries and to dislocated shoulders when they attempt moves on harder snow. Both skiers and snowboarders are most likely to have accidents on the third or fourth day of a week-long holiday due to tiredness caused by the high altitude and constant activity.

COST   

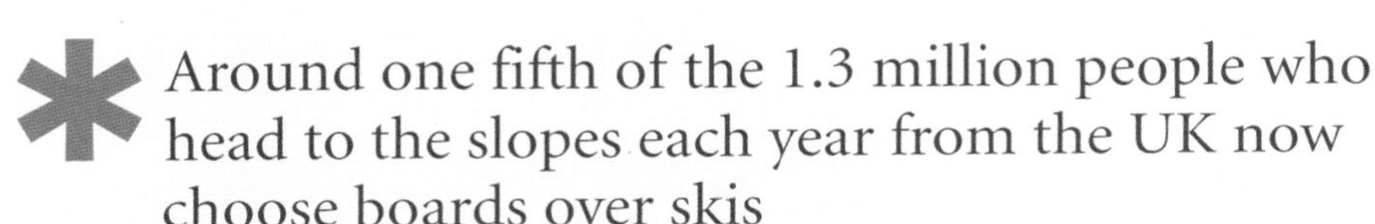

Around one fifth of the 1.3 million people who head to the slopes each year from the UK now choose boards over skis

Image courtesy of Snowsport GB

* Physiologists claim this is the most physically demanding of all activities

and more comfortable than the downhill variety. Two types of wax are applied to cross-country skis – glide wax reduces friction between the ski and snow and kick wax, used only in the classic technique, prevents skis from slipping.

BODY BOOSTER

■ **Muscles** – 80 per cent of the body's muscles are utilised in this activity – more than in any other sport. As the skier propels themselves along, they must engage the muscles in the legs, back, shoulders and arms, particularly the backs of the upper arms. Effort is even more pronounced when 'double-poling' (moving both poles together in parallel).

■ **Calories** – Cross-country skiing devours calories. At a very slow pace you can burn 435 calories per hour. Speed up to a moderate pace and that increases to 472-563 calories. Elite skiers, who cover snowy paths at 40 mph on the downhills and 15-20 mph on the flat, can expend a colossal 985 calories an hour.

■ **Cardiovascular system** – Because of the effort it requires, this sport taxes the heart and lungs in the most beneficial way. Several of the world's best marathon runners (including Grete Weitz and Ingrid Kristiansen) were keen cross-country skiers.

RISK FACTOR

Scandinavian research reports a high rate of lower back pain among high-level cross-country skiers with some studies showing that up to two thirds of racers experience it at some time. However, this problem is not associated with recreational skiing and is linked to the diagonal racing style of movement as opposed to the skating approach.

COST   

Image courtesy of Plas y Brenin, pyb.co.uk

8

MOUNTAIN BIKING

The 'mountain' in mountain biking is, in fact, somewhat misleading as the term simply refers to any cycling that is done off-road. If you have hills nearby, all the better, as variety is the key in this sport, but it can be enjoyed anywhere from forest tracks, coastal paths, open moorlands to hills and, yes, on mountainous terrain. It first became popular in the 1970s when cyclists began modifying their existing bikes to enable them to be used in off-road downhill races. There are now four main disciplines in competitive mountain biking. Downhill racing is about who is the fastest from top to bottom of a hair-raising course. Four-cross (or 4X) riders compete on challenging courses that include a mix of natural and man-made obstacles covering a steep descent. They are designed to last between 25 seconds and one minute and are usually fast and frenzied. Cross-country races typically take place on a marked lap of one to three miles and involve climbing, descending, single-track and technical sections (tight turns or difficult terrain). Finally, trailquest combines cross-country mountain biking with orienteering – competitors must search for specific locations in forests and clip special cards as evidence of their visit.

HOW TO DO IT

If you can ride a bike you can ride a mountain bike. Check your seat position is correct before you set off – your extended leg, at the bottom of the pedal stroke, should be almost straight, otherwise you might be prone to leg cramps and will find pedalling efficiency suffers. On flatter surfaces, keep pedal speed constant for comfort – aim for around 60-70 revolutions per minute to maximise blood flow to tiring limbs.

According to the charity Sustrans, around 75 per cent of Britons live within two miles of the National Cycle Network of off-road paths, which is often a good place to gain confidence if you haven't taken to two wheels in a while. After that, though, you can graduate to more challenging climbs and routes, going totally 'off-piste' in the mountains should you choose. On the whole, however, it is important stick to designated mountain bike trails away from horses and walkers.

A huge attraction of mountain biking is the social aspect of the sport. Even if you don't choose to join a cycling club, there are likely to be many informal groups heading to the hills in your area (ask you local council or bike shop for details).

EQUIPMENT

When buying your first mountain bike, look for an all-terrain model with fat (40 to 60 mm) knobbly tyres for cushioning on rough surfaces, very low

Image courtesy of Go Fast! Sports

gears to overcome the drag of ploughing through loose material while climbing steep gradients, straight handlebars for wrenching the front wheel around obstacles, disc brakes and at least front suspension. A basic mountain bike will not cost you the earth, however, the more you pay the more you get for your money. The best mountain bikes combine lightness and durability and the more you spend the better the ratio of these will be. As you progress, you may wish to switch from an all-terrain bike to one that better suits your individual needs such as a downhill bike with different levels of suspension.

Bike maintenance is an essential part of this sport – your bike will needed to be thoroughly cleaned after every off-road ride and will also need a regular health-check. Although cycle shops offer such a service, it is worth knowing the basics yourself. A safety helmet and padded cycling shorts are useful additions to your wardrobe if you cycle regularly.

BODY BOOSTING

■ **Muscles** – The pedalling action works most of the main muscles in the legs including the quadriceps, calf and gluteus maximus muscles in your buttocks, as well as strengthening your tendons without the load bearing stress of something like running.

■ **Calories** – Coasting on flat ground at 30 mph will burn around two calories a minute; switch to biking on undulating terrain and tough conditions and that can increase to 15 calories a minute.

■ **Cardiovascular system** – Your heart and lungs are perhaps the biggest beneficiaries of regular cycling. Pedalling works the cardiovascular system, which will operate more efficiently as you get fitter.

RISK FACTOR

Cyclists are more likely to be injured on roads than on hills, but that doesn't mean there is any less risk of falling off. Uneven terrain and bumpy earth can throw someone out of the saddle quite easily, so a helmet is essential. For men, the health benefits of regular cycling carry a troublesome trade-off. Too many hours on a bicycle saddle have been shown to compress the artery and vital nerves leading to the penis, increasing the risk of numbness, pain, and erectile dysfunction. Ask in cycling shops for padded cycling shorts and for more comfortable, cushioned saddles developed to lower this risk.

COST  

Image courtesy of Plas y Brenin, pyb.co.uk

On flatter surfaces, keep pedal speed constant for comfort – aim for around 60-70 revolutions per minute

ORIENTEERING

Known as 'cunning running', because it makes you think on your feet, orienteering takes place on mountains or fells, forests or moors and involves getting from A to B on foot (while running or walking), with the help of a compass and detailed map and passing through a series of control points, in the quickest time possible.

HOW TO DO IT

The best way to start is to become a member of one of the 120 clubs affiliated to British Orienteering around the UK. These are inexpensive to join and provide coaching as well as entry to events and leagues. In order to race, you will need to be fit enough to walk at a good pace for up to an hour over undulating terrain, but apart from this you can compete at whatever speed you like. Top orienteers are extremely fit runners, many of whom also compete in other running sports, but there are large numbers of participants who prefer to take their time and enjoy the scenery. For many, the main challenge is map-reading their way from check-point to check-point. At each control point is an orange and white flag along with a manual or electronic punch, which records that you have visited the point. The winner is the person who visits the correct controls in the right order and the quickest time.

Courses vary between three and 15 km in length, depending on your age and level of experience, and the larger events are divided into classifications for everyone from the under 10s to the over 75s. While you can train for orienteering on your own, its attraction is the competitive element, which is provided in these organised events.

EQUIPMENT

All you need is a pair of trainers or all-terrain shoes with good grip and outdoor clothes including a waterproof jacket. At most orienteering competitions, full body cover (ie. covering the arms, legs and torso) is compulsory. A compass is useful, but not essential for beginners, and at most big events it's possible to buy all the kit you need. The map you need will be provided at the event.

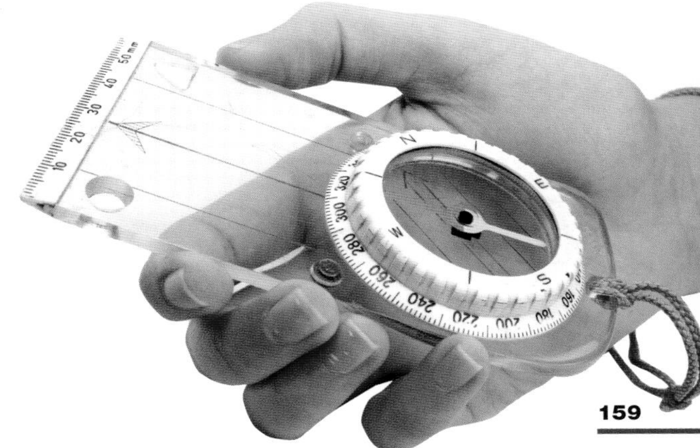

Both images courtesy of British Orienteering

BODY BOOSTING

■ **Muscles** – As with any form of running, the leg muscles are the major ones worked. Orienteering with its twists and turns, is particularly good at strengthening the muscles below the knee.

■ **Calories** – A 10-stone person can expect to burn between 440 and 575 calories an hour.

■ **Mind** – Research has found that ageing orienteers, compared with non-athletes, had faster reaction speeds and better attention skills.

RISK FACTOR

Getting lost is the main risk, particularly in woods and forests, where it is easy for beginners to lose their sense of direction. It is recommended that beginners use obvious features of the terrain such as walls, fences, streams to find a route back to the start if a map-reading error is made. Because orienteering generally takes place in woodland, getting cuts and grazes are a risk.

COST  

FELL RUNNING

Fells are the collective name for mountains, moors and hills, and this sport (sometimes called mountain running) is a kind of extreme cross-country, for the sturdiest of runners. The sport is well established in the north of England, Scotland and Ireland, with an enthusiastic racing and club set-up in just about all regions of the country except for the flat lands around East Anglia and Lincolnshire. Races take place all year round and are categorised according to steepness and difficulty, ranging from short dashes to the top of a peak and back down to long circuits covering a number of hills. Should you become ultra keen, there are two-day events known as Mountain Marathons where navigational ability, powers of endurance and survival skills are put to the ultimate test. You can also take part in the Ben Nevis race, an annual run up the 4,406-foot peak of Britain's biggest mountain, covering terrain that is difficult to even walk on.

This is a sport that will appeal to anyone who loves mountains and who wants to run up one 'just because it's there'.

HOW TO DO IT

Clearly, you need to be reasonably fit to try it, although there are introductory races for all abilities and there is no shame in walking up some of the steeper sections of a course. Joining a club will get you expert coaching. If there isn't a fell club nearby, join an athletic club with a strong cross-country section, as many of the members will also enter fell races, and the club will provide the appropriate training.

Fell running technique focuses primarily on rhythm – allow a hill to break your stride and you will slow down dramatically, so shorten your stride and take 'baby steps' when running uphill. Your posture should be upright with your head, shoulders and back forming a straight line over the feet – don't lean forward from the waist or back. Keep your arms bent at right angles and use them to 'pump' you forwards. If the hill is long or the gradient increases, keep shortening your stride to maintain a smooth and efficient breathing pattern. In many ways running down steep hills is trickier to master. Many people make the mistake of running too fast, resulting in severe muscle soreness, or they're so hesitant to surrender to gravity that they slam their feet down as if to brake which tires the quadriceps muscles. Try not to let your feet slap on the ground or reach too far forward. Keep an upright body posture, and as you move faster, aim to take more steps rather than longer strides. Having strong core muscles is crucial to good control on hills. If you find your back aches or spasms during or after a run, then weak core muscles is usually the reason.

EQUIPMENT

You will need a good pair of waterproof fell shoes that are supple but also allow your feet to grip an uneven, slippery surface. Many of the latest have small rubber studs in the soles for added traction. Regulations on fell running have been tightened up recently and it is advisable to take a map, whistle, compass, waterproof and windproof top and bottoms out with you.

BODY BOOSTING

- **Calories** – A great sport for calorie burning – expect to burn in excess of 560 an hour.
- **Muscles** – Running uphill forces the muscles in your hips, legs, ankles and feet to contract in a coordinated fashion while supporting your full body weight as they attempt to overcome gravity and get you up the hill. Studies have shown that fell runners have much higher concentrations of aerobic enzymes – the chemicals which allow muscles to function at high intensity for long periods without fatigue – in their quadriceps muscles at the front of the thigh than those who did all their running on flat terrain.
- **Heart** – Researchers have found that running uphill gives you a cardiovascular workout and lowers triglycerides (blood fats) that are a risk factor for heart disease, whilst downhill running has proven better for lowering blood sugar levels that can cause diabetes.

RISK FACTOR

Safety is an issue with fell running. It's important to have the right equipment and check the weather before you go out. The usual hiker's procedure of letting someone know where you'll be and what time you'll be back are good precautions. Downhill running can place strain on the knees and be difficult for those with knee problems.

COST 

Both photographs by Britta Sendlhofer

ROCK CLIMBING

There is a real adrenaline surge that comes from conquering a rock face, however small or large, and climbing is among the fastest growing sports in the UK. Membership of the British Mountaineering Council (BMC), the sport's governing body, has nearly doubled in the last 10 years and there are currently around 63,000 climbing club members in the UK, with the proportion of women climbers on the rise from 16 per cent to 25 per cent in the past few years. The impressive numbers of newcomers to the sport is undoubtedly linked to the fact that Britain's rock climbing venues now have a reputation as among the best in the world. We may not have the highest ascents, but in terms of variety, the opportunities here are enormous. There is sea-cliff climbing in Devon and Cornwall, granite crags in Sennan and Bosgran and climbs for every level and ability in the Peak and Lake Districts. In North Wales and the Snowdonia National Park there are climbing centres at every turn, while Scotland offers less crowded but equally exhilarating climbing highlights, particularly in the Cairngorms.

HOW TO DO IT

No climber is required to take a course before heading up a rock face, but you face obvious risks if you don't. It is best to start at a local climbing centre or one of the 300-plus clubs affiliated to the BMC. An option is to head for a week-long 'learn to climb' course in one of the country's climbing hotspots such as the Peak District (which has 10,000 recorded climbs) or North Wales. In these, you will learn the basics of rope work, belaying and anchoring skills as well as how to look after yourself and your rock climbing buddies. Bouldering – climbing low off the ground with no ropes – is a great way to practise your technique and build up your strength. If you decide the sport is for you, there are many advantages of becoming a climbing club member – not least the fact that you will get lessons, insurance and endless information about where to climb and how to do so safely.

A good basic level of cardiovascular fitness is needed before you start and you will need to strengthen your forearms and fingers. Try static hangs, where you support your body weight by hanging with one arm. However, the best climbers aren't necessarily the most athletic – climbing is about technique, not simply physical ability and strength.

EQUIPMENT

A minor downside of climbing is the shopping list – you need to invest in a lot of kit if you want to take it anything approaching seriously. Wear loose-fitting,

Image courtesy of Plas y Brenin, pyb.co.uk

* There is a real adrenaline surge that comes from conquering a rock face

waterproof clothes and good footwear – trainers can be worn but you will find it much easier with a pair of specialist climbing shoes. Aside from that, there is the harness (to secure you in a seated position), helmet (a vital safety item of safety), ropes (you will need a variety), cams (spring-loaded camming devices that are used to anchor you to the cracks of rocks) and carabineers (needed for just about everything in climbing) and so the list goes on … Expect to pay at least a couple of hundred pounds on the basics.

BODY BOOSTING

■ **Muscles** – Climbers will quickly begin to develop arm, back, finger, and core strength as a result of the many reaches and holds that are repeated over and over through the completion of one climb.
■ **Calories** – Going up uses more energy than going forward or down, and you will burn between 390 and 475 calories in an hour if you climb at a steady rate.
■ **Joints** – You will develop tremendous flexibility in the hips, knees and shoulders.

■ **Mind** – Each climb is like a puzzle, and regular climbing develops concentration, focus and determination. The better a climber you become, the better your ability to assess a problem, look for a solution and then execute a plan to reach the top. Beginners usually pick their route hold by hold, but as you become more accomplished, you will find that you are able to look ahead and visualise the bigger picture – an experienced climber can keep an entire route in his mind as he climbs.

RISK FACTOR

Falling is a risk in climbing, but a good school will make sure you are taught proper safety procedures. When falls do happen, it is usually as a result of being tired, dehydrated and exposed to extreme temperatures, causing coordination to deteriorate and muscles to fatigue.

Injuries caused by other means are actually more common. Collateral ligament strain – caused by ligaments being pulled away from the bone – is a frequent complaint, particularly in the fingers, which are used to repeatedly pull the body up the rock face. Another medical condition called Lateral Epicondylitis can cause pain in the forearm and elbow and is usually triggered by repetitive grabbing and pulling that strains tendons in the arms. You also need to be aware of debris and rocks that can be loosened and fall on you and your fellow climbers as you ascend.

COST   

Both images courtesy of Plas y Brenin, pyb.co.uk

POTHOLING

Fancy squeezing yourself between a rock and a hard place and then heading down into the deepest, darkest recesses of the world? This is not a sport for the anxiously disposed – and the prospect of descending into a damp, dark closed space incites terror in many. However, if you can get over the initial fear, potholing can be an extremely rewarding experience. Caves comprise some of the last unexplored regions in the world, and potholing can combine the adrenaline rush of extreme physical activity with the sense of discovery of a totally alien underworld.

HOW TO DO IT

This is an activity where guides and lessons – which are relatively expensive (up to £100 for a beginner session) – are paramount. There are potholing centres all around the UK where you can enter underground caves with an instructor, but among the best are those in the Peak District and Yorkshire Dales.

Getting into a cave is often the most difficult part of the whole experience. Many cave entrances are small or involve vertical drops into which you must either abseil or climb down ladders. Inside, experienced cavers follow natural water courses and use maps to navigate. It is a minefield: There are pitches (or drops) where you must either climb, abseil or use a lightweight rolled-up steel ladder, but by far the worst prospect for anyone of a slightly nervous disposition are the 'squeezes' that can be a tiny tunnel between two rock faces, about 12 inches high, not a lot wider, and up to 20 metres long. Because there is water on the ground, you must crawl along on your stomach with your cheek pressed against mud.

In theory, you can go potholing on your own, but it is certainly not advisable, even for those who have a high level of experience. Good preparation, organisation and leadership skills are vital to stay safe.

EQUIPMENT

You will need a body fleece for warmth with a tough and stiff outer layer for protection, wetsocks to keep the feet warm, and wellies for grip and protection. Absolute essentials include the helmet, the headlamp, safety harnesses (for novices) and the ropes used to ascend or descend vertical pitches. A first-aid kit should also be taken. All will be provided by the outdoor activity centre that takes you potholing.

BODY BOOSTING

■ **Muscles** – Much depends on the conditions, but potholing will generally engage the core muscles as well as those in the arms, wrists, fingers and legs.
■ **Calories** – You could burn anything between 180 and 320 calories an hour underground, the higher

Image courtesy of Black Mountain Activities

amount more likely if it is cold and wet and your body is working extra hard to stay warm.

■ **Mind** – Potholing is hard work on the old grey matter. When you are not concentrating so hard on where to go next in the black abyss ahead, you are gripped with a sense of fear or euphoria about how you managed to get where you are. Needless to say, confidence and self-esteem soar with regular potholing.

RISK FACTOR

Given the obvious dangers of squeezing yourself through extremely small spaces, sometimes filled with water, the accident rate involving cavers is quite low. However, when accidents do happen, they can be serious which is why someone who is qualified to use medical equipment should be always be part of the party. Among the main dangers are falling, hypothermia, flooding and physical exhaustion. Rescues from an underground location are difficult and need to be carried out by teams of trained cave rescuers, using specialised equipment.

COST   

GORGE WALKING

Known by a host of different names including ghyll (the northern term for a narrow mountain stream) scrambling, gully bashing and stream walking, this is one of the most popular sports on offer at outdoor activity centres in the UK. Described as 'caving with the roof off', you literally walk (or scramble) your way down waterfalls, gorges, tricky rock traverses, over obstacles and into plunge pools. It is not essential to be a strong swimmer (your buoyancy aid will keep you afloat), but a degree of water confidence is essential.

HOW TO DO IT

Joining an organised gorge walking trip is the only way to start. Many outdoor centres cater for families or children as young as seven on their own, offering a gentle introduction and plenty of fun. On these beginners' walks, you needn't always get very wet, as you walk along at a relaxed pace, exploring caves and caverns en route. But for those seeking a greater thrill, wet gorge walking is the next step up. Your introduction to a day of water wading is likely to include a small traverse, a jump in to the river and a swim across to the far side.

EQUIPMENT

Activity centres will equip you with wetsuit, buoyancy aid and helmet. Aside from that you will need a swimsuit to wear beneath a wetsuit (although not strictly essential they are often provided by centres) – otherwise waterproof clothing will suffice, and either a good pair of walking boots or trainers with a well-gripping sole. Wear warm layers of clothing – a jumper or fleece and waterproof jacket are essential – and remember to take a change of clothing and a towel for when you finish.

BODY BOOSTING

■ **Muscles** – Water is 800 times denser than air and provides up to twelve times the resistance you get on land, so your legs will get a tough workout. If you try waterfall climbing, your arms and upper body will be tested too. This activity can be exhausting.

■ **Calories** – This is tough – expect to use 458-513 calories an hour.

RISK FACTOR

There is no national governing body for gorge walking, which means there are no safety standards to adhere to. However, the importance of attending a course with well-qualified instructors cannot be overstated – go out with groups where there is a maximum of eight people to one instructor. Wet rocks can become extremely slippery, particularly at venues which are seldom used, and falls are common.

COST  

Image courtesy of Plas y Brenin, pyb.co.uk

BOG TROTTING

Peculiar to the Peak District, this group activity takes place on remote peat moorlands covered in heather. It is best described as walking through wet porridge with the heavily dissected peat blanket moist and squelchy underfoot. The organisers insist participants have a good level of fitness – using walking poles to help keep you upright, you will require nimble footwork to keep you from sinking – and even then, be prepared to traverse some areas of bogland on your hands and knees. It's messy and exhausting, but the remote moonscape of the highest plateaus of the Peak District National Park is not to be missed.

CHAPTER 5
WILD GYM THE NEXT LEVEL

You all look like happy campers to me.
Happy campers you are, happy campers you
have been, and, as far as I am concerned,
happy campers you will always be

Dan Quayle

Image courtesy of the Countryside Alliance

WILD GYMS ARE NOT JUST A MEANS OF GETTING FIT or escaping from stress and tension: they can become a way of life. Once you begin to embrace that philosophy, you will find you want to explore the parameters of the outdoors in every way. This chapter will hopefully provide some inspiration as to the endless ways you can expand your wild gym horizons.

Progression is the key to continued participation in sport. Setting new goals and aspiring to reach them keeps people motivated and interested, while plugging away at the same level, same activity conducted in the same venue is the most likely route to boredom and the hanging up of one's boots, trainers or other equipment.

Certainly, the biggest attraction of outdoor exercise is its diversity. Your experience of many of the wild gym activities detailed in the previous chapters will only be enhanced if you try them in different locations or with different people. There are limitless opportunities for variety and change. Take along the family, head abroad or take your wild gym to previously unexplored territories. Most importantly, wherever you go and whoever you take, make sure your wild gym philosophy goes with you.

WILD GYM WITH THE FAMILY

Children are naturally inclined to play outdoors. It is habit and society's influence that increasingly draws them inside and retains them within the confines of four walls. By making outdoor activities exciting and demonstrating that they can be done with parents or friends, children's eyes can be opened to the wild and wonderful world outside.

Many of the activities mentioned previously cater for all age groups and abilities. It is always wise to check with sports governing bodies or activity centres to see whether they have provisions for children and, for more adventurous pursuits, it is definitely worth consulting the Adventure Activities Licensing Authority to see that safety standards are met for children. Some wild gym pursuits specifically target families and are a great introduction to an active lifestyle. Here are a few to get you started:

Image courtesy of British Orienteering

DINGHY SAILING

Sailing is sociable, fun and something the entire family can do together, once everyone has a grounding in the fundamentals of handling a boat. A two-day Royal Yachting Association (RYA) Level One course will take children aged eight and up, who have never set sail before, through the basics of sailing a dinghy (a small boat), teaching them boat control, rigging and safety skills. Much of the 48 hours is spent afloat learning manoeuvres, and by the end of the course they will be able to helm a dinghy under the supervision of an instructor.

Dinghy sailing is ideal for youngsters because it's relatively easy to learn and requires little outlay in terms of equipment at the start. All they will need are some non-slip shoes, a swimming costume and full-length trousers (although not jeans) along with their sense of seafaring adventure. Younger children will require an adult to accompany them, and this is something the whole family can learn together.

BALLOONING

For real escapism as a family, there can be nothing as magical as floating elegantly across the countryside in a hot air balloon. Reaching heights of 1,200 metres and floating along at 10 mph with only a huge burning flame released every 30 seconds or so to keep you air-bound, you might think the activity too risky to introduce to children. However, it is statistically one of the safest forms of air travel – your balloon 'pilot' will be a fully qualified commercial pilot and all flights are carried out in accordance with strict guidelines set out and monitored by the Civil Aviation Authority. Generally, children need to be at least 10 years old (or 4'6" / 1.4m tall) – any younger and they are too small to see out of the sides of the basket – and should be accompanied by at least one adult. It can be an expensive experience (costing up to £150 per passenger), but surely one that will never be forgotten. Warm clothes are essential (it's cold up there however balmy a day it seems on the ground) and binoculars are useful. Apart from that, enjoy the view.

BUSHCRAFT

Allowing your child to handle sharp knives and eat unusual wild plants sounds like a recipe for danger and disaster, yet the family versions of the bushcraft and survival courses held for adults (see Wild Gym to Go) are great for building kids' confidence levels and for

* There can be nothing as magical as floating elegantly across the countryside in a hot air balloon

introducing them to the thrill of the outdoors. Some are even accredited with the Duke of Edinburgh's Award Scheme. Depending on where you go, the skills taught will vary from friction fire lighting to knife-sharpening, primitive fishing, setting traps and hunting for berries and edible fruit. Most accept children from the age of seven upwards (some insist they are accompanied by an adult) and take place over one to four days, often involving camping at night in self-made shelters. If it all sounds too Grizzly Adams, be aware that these camps are geared for youngsters and that family games are interspersed with the learning of rudimentary skills.

WHITE WATER RAFTING

If your teenager is easily bored by family activities, you might want to introduce them to the thrills of white-water rafting. Generally offered to children aged 14 and over, this experience is available at activity centres around the country, and is not for the faint-hearted. Among the best venues is the National Watersports Centre, Holme Pierrepont, Nottinghamshire, where a Grade Three (meaning it is among the most testing), man-made, custom-built white water rafting course will put even seasoned adrenaline junkies through their paces. Each session lasts for two hours, during which a qualified instructor will steer inflatable rafts holding between four and eight passengers who will undoubtedly find the speed and volume of their descent exhilarating. If they get hooked, they can progress to try the same white-water course in a two-man canoe.

Left: Image courtesy of UK Survival School

WILD GYM TO GO

For many, the biggest attraction of wild gyms over their indoor counterparts is that they are transportable. If you have the enthusiasm and inclination, you can transfer your experience anywhere you want. Often, sports and activities have an international base that means you will be able to practise them the world over. Likewise, many of the organisations featured in the directory section will arrange tailored holiday experiences for people who are keen to try out their wild gym overseas.

CAMPING

Clearly not a physical activity in the blood, sweat and tears sense, camping has been included because it provides the ideal base from which to launch so many wild gym weekends in the UK and overseas.

There are two schools of thought about camping. One is that it is the experience of being outdoors, sleeping beneath the stars and connecting with nature that counts. For these hardcore campers, nothing beats erecting a tent in a field with only goats and a stream for company – and if it rains, so be it. The second school of thought is that a tent is all very well in the sun, but given the variable weather in Britain, knee-deep mud and soggy sleeping bags are risks best avoided.

For those who have been scarred by previous attempts at tent-based holidays or who simply can't be bothered to untangle the poles and carcass of their tent, there is good news indeed. Camping, it seems, has gone somewhat upmarket, even glamorous, having earned it the nickname of 'glamping' by some. Gypsy caravans, updated and modernised youth hostels, yurts and teepees all enter into the spirit of camping (many still requiring a camping stove and sleeping bag), but eliminate at least some of the possible hassles and discomforts of outdoor living. These alternative camping options are now on offer all around the country, and will appeal to anyone who doesn't mind showering in freezing water, but who sees no point in exposing themselves to any greater hardship. What you can now get is alfresco pleasure without the pain.

Image courtesy of LaRosa

* A typical day begins with a pre-breakfast beach stretching session followed by a swim in Watamu's crystal waters

Image courtesy of Wild Fitness

ADVENTURE FITNESS

Countless tour operators run adventure packages where you can try everything from white water rafting in France to bungee jumping in New Zealand, and if you have a specific wild gym holiday in mind, it's only ever a Google search away. However, if you're more interested in general fitness in a beautiful outdoor location, Wild Fitness might be the answer. This is a relatively new concept introduced by London-based sportswoman Tara Wood, in which a strict fitness regime on an African coastline allows you to experience the adrenaline rush and return home with a super-toned physique.

Courses take place in a sleepy fishing village on the north coast of Kenya overlooking the Indian Ocean that is teeming with coral reefs stretching back to the Sokoke forest reserve. What sets it apart from spa resorts and posh hotels is the workout programme. A typical day begins with a pre-breakfast (6.30am – gulp), beach stretching session followed by a swim in Watamu's crystal waters and might include anything from postural assessments by physical therapists to boxing sessions and barefoot sand running (see page 80). Primal skills circuits – lunging, throwing, pushing and twisting – provide a glimpse into the pre-obesity world of our ancestors while snorkelling, beach circuits and running sessions through palm forest and mangrove all feature on the itinerary. It is perhaps stating the obvious to suggest this is not a holiday for couch potatoes.

SURVIVAL COURSES

If you think Tom and Barbara Good took self-sufficiency to extremes, you might want to skip this entry. At serious survival schools the aim is to dispel any romantic ideal of 'living off the land'. Usually on these courses, if you don't hunt and forage you don't eat, so skills picked up rather swiftly include the ability to determine whether fungi are friend or foe, how to filter and purify water and how to make (and use) hunting weapons for trapping and snaring animals. Some teach realistic survival skills such as using condoms for water carriers, sending distress signals and first aid, while many offer a slightly gentler introduction to the whole scene including one-day navigation and signalling courses. They are no place for slaves of supermarkets and other conveniences of modern living, or anyone likely to miss the most basic of home comforts. It is no coincidence that many survival courses are held in rural backwaters. Expect cold temperatures, mud and fatigue. Then double it.

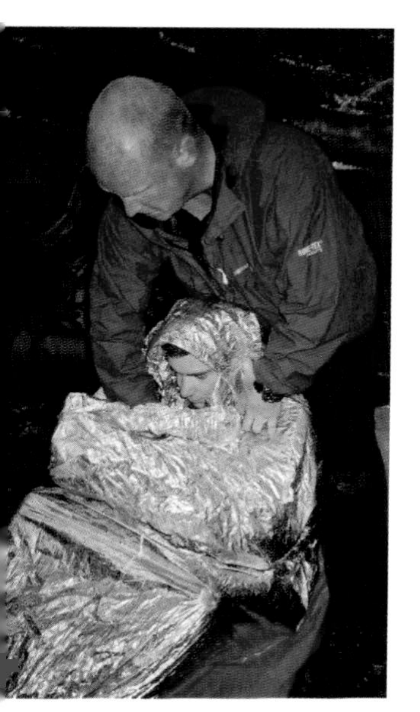

On the plus side, you will learn the core skills of wilderness living that were second nature to our ancestors – how to light fire through friction, practise native hunting and fishing techniques including trapping, angling, spearing and netting, and how to build your own wind and water-tight shelter. They last anywhere from a day to two weeks, and take place in the unpredictable and undeniably demanding environment of some of the wildest terrain in Britain. You don't need much experience to try surviving in the wild. If you have camped before it will hold you in good stead, but far more important is the ability to abandon preconceptions and get stuck in.

Image courtesy of UK Survival School

Image courtesy of Snowdonia Adventures

NAVIGATION SKILLS

In any woodland setting and for wild gym activities as diverse as orienteering, climbing and hiking, map reading is an essential skill. Without it you could end up at the very least frustrated by your progress or, worse, hopelessly lost in an alien environment.

A great way to hone your navigational abilities is to enrol on the National Navigation Award Scheme for which you need no prior experience. Following tuition from experts, a bronze award is given to those who can navigate paths and tracks using basic map skills and compass work for a distance of two to five kilometres. The silver level is awarded for more accurate compass work and the ability to apply the appropriate navigational techniques for finding your way cross-country over a distance of five to eight kilometres. To get the gold award, you'll need the skills for dealing with complex contour features on maps and using them to navigate a six to 10 kilometre course. There is also instruction in navigating at night and walking or hiking by torchlight, which can add a whole new adrenaline shot to your adventure. None of these certificates catapults you to instructor level, but they will enhance your confidence and intrepidness several-fold.

WOODLAND LIVING

If you can find your way around the local woods – at day or night – how about living off them? Less challenging than the survival schools (see page 182), there are several venues in the UK and abroad where you can learn the wonders of indulging in wilderness gourmet from gutting and jointing fresh game to making real herbal teas and dandelion salads. Weekend wilderness cookery courses teach you how to create a woodland kitchen, cook in one pot and with no utensils and prepare a three-course feast for your camp-mates.

Photograph by Louis Quail, courtesy of River Cottage HQ

For a more extreme challenge, some companies now run arctic survival vacations – in which you learn to ice fish and track and trap for food – or courses in jungle wilderness skills where indigenous tribesmen from Borneo and other regions teach the skills passed down through generations such as using bamboo craft for shelter, making traditional medicines, selecting edible fruits from the environment and hunting for animals.

Photograph by Rob Howard, courtesy of TrailPlus

WILD GYM EXTREME

If you have dipped your toe into the water and mud of the great outdoors and now you are seeking a tougher challenge, more thrilling adventures and a test to push you to new limits, then extreme wild gym activities are worth exploring. There are sports and activities out there that will sap your endurance, stamina and physical strength while taking you on a white-knuckle, adrenaline-surging adventure like nothing you have ever experienced. And you are not alone – according to Sport England extreme activities are soaring in popularity at a faster rate than more traditional sports. Around one in seven adults now try an adventure sport every year.

But before you get stuck in, a few words of caution. To some extent, all outdoor activities carry an element of risk, and their unpredictability is very much part of their appeal. But extreme wild gym exploits, in particular, require careful planning and a little research in advance. It is inadvisable to try any of these thrilling but formidable activities without the guidance of a qualified expert who is experienced in handling the diverse and potentially lethal conditions you might encounter. Pay particular attention to weather conditions, make sure you have adequate equipment and heed the safety precautions. If you are in any way concerned about the quality of tuition or standards of teaching, err on the side of caution and select a more reputable instructor or course. Otherwise, hold on tight and enjoy the ride.

NIGHT CYCLING

Night cycling (also called night biking and night riding) is becoming hugely popular in the UK, America and Europe with many companies organising night bike tours in diverse locations. The speed of cycling combined with the thrill of danger resulting from limited visibility is at the heart of this sport. For beginners, there are city rides conducted at night when cars – the biker's nemesis – are most easily avoided. In Paris, organised tours take you around the city's cycle-friendly streets and tourist attractions on a two-hour night ride.

New Yorkers meet at 10pm on the first Friday of every month at the southwest corner of Central Park (Columbus circle) to take part in the Central Park Moonlight Ride, and the Midnight Ridazz in Los Angeles attracts 800 cyclists on the second Friday of each month for themed rides through the streets of the city. The Dead Celebrities tour takes cyclists to sites of the deaths of famous people, while the Prom Night tour requires participants to wear tuxedos and ball gowns. The Midnight Ridazz riders meet at Echo Park and Sunset Boulevard at 9.30pm to commence cycling at 10pm.

Off road night biking, however, remains the ultimate test. Cities have their own illumination, but when it's dark in forests and fields, it's very dark. Imagine descending a hill in a forest at speed, spotting trees only with the light of your mountain bike and unable to determine where the ground dips and undulates and you have an inkling of the thrill – terror, even – involved. Even trails and routes you have ridden countless times during daylight can present different and unexpected challenges in the dark. The slightest bump over a tree-root can seem ten times worse when you hit it while trying to control your speed and hold your nerve because you can't see in front of you. This is not an activity to try on your own, and the immense number of night riding tours in venues as diverse as Wales, Scotland and the South Downs are well worth the effort and relatively little expense.

Image courtesy of Forest Freeride

Other than the usual mountain biking equipment (see page 155), you will need good reflective clothing and by law you need a back red reflector as well as front and rear lights on your bike. Most bikes manufactured after 1985 now come fitted with white reflectors on both wheels and amber ones on the pedals but if yours isn't, then it is wise to invest in some.

COASTEERING

Claw your way along cliff edges, scramble across rocks to the water's edge and then launch yourself off the side into freezing cold water without a harness or paddle to assist you. If this sounds to you like something you'd have to be insane or suicidal to try, you'll be surprised to hear that coasteering is in fact an extremely popular sport in the UK. This is, unsurprisingly, not something to without supervision and instruction, and such are the safety concerns that the British Coasteering Federation Award was set up recently to ensure those who offer courses adhere to strict standards. Sessions should be led by a minimum of two qualified coasteer guides who should hold the British Coasteering Federation Award, a valid Beach Lifeguard Award, an up-to-date First Aid Certificate and have considerable knowledge of the location. Your experience will include a combination of swimming along the base of the cliffs as well as exploring gullies, caves, cracks and different rock formations created by the sea. Do not expect an easy ride. Traversing the ground requires considerable effort and energy as does climbing the cliffs to the jumping locations. Then there's the leap itself. Cliff jumps can

Image courtesy of Snowdonia Adventures

range from two to 10 metres in height and good technique is vital to your enjoyment. Experts suggest looking out to sea, rather than looking downwards as you launch yourself off the rocks. Regular coasteerers develop extremely strong leg muscles from both climbing and jumping. Because the sea is so unpredictable, it is impossible to foresee quite what will happen when you hit the water. If there are sudden waves, you will need to scramble to safety while snorting seawater from your nostrils. If the water is still, you might bob along gently back to your starting place. Much of the thrill is in expecting the unexpected and pushing your body to exhaustive extremes – this is as physically challenging as it is mentally. Equipment-wise you will need a swimsuit beneath a full body wetsuit, buoyancy aid, helmet and suitable footwear that is waterproof and grips the wet rock surfaces well – most of these will be provided by the outdoor centre you attend.

FREE FALL ABESEILING AND RAP RUNNING

You may have tried abseiling, but have you tried it without the rock face? Free-fall abseiling (also called freefall rappelling) is a descent by rope without a wall on which to guide yourself down. This is the method of deployment into buildings and down from helicopters that is widely used by special services, and needless to say, it is faster and more frightening than the conventional form of the activity. Since it basically involves you dangling from a rope at great height, safety procedures are vital, and a huge assortment of ropes and harnesses are used to ensure you descend harm-free. Its relative, rap running, is about-turn abseiling performed while facing forwards. It is not for the fainthearted although, oddly, a fear of heights should not be considered too great a barrier to this activity as most centres offer a variety of descents that begin with the very gentle.

Both activities require colossal mental application and a good degree of strength, particularly in the core muscles as you try to steady yourself in the rope. Rap-running requires strong leg muscles, more so than regular abseiling, as it is hard work descending the rock face head first and your legs are the only thing to keep you in place. Courses in both freefall abseiling and rap running generally last a half or full day and will take you through the basics of conventional abseiling to boost your confidence.

Photograph by Ben Dawson of gliderpilot.co.uk

GLIDING

Driving a plane without an engine, relying on thermals and air currents to keep you in the sky, is billed by enthusiasts as the closest experience you can get to flying like a bird. There are 77,000 regular gliding participants in the UK and with almost one hundred clubs, the sport is growing in popularity. According to the British Gliding Association, no great skill is required to master the basics – in fact, the association likens the level of aptitude to that required for driving a car.

Although weather conditions are important, there are only three things that prevent flying in a glider: rain, low cloud and winds of more than 30 mph. To get airbound your glider is

winched at great speed on one wheel until, just like a kite at the end of a rope, you are suddenly in the air. When you're at the required altitude, you release the line and before you realise it you are flying. To stay up, you need to find air that is rising, of which there are three forms – thermals, ridge (or hill) lifts and waves.

Joining a club will not only provide tuition and competition, but the rather essential (and otherwise expensive) equipment. Most clubs will have two-seaters for instructional purposes and single-seaters available for when you progress to flying solo. You will also be provided with the essential parachute, beneath which you should wear lightweight, comfortable clothing. Sunglasses are essential. Trial lessons cost as little as £25 (which usually includes temporary month-long membership of a club) rising to £250 for a week-long course.

Pretty much anyone over the age of 16 can try this sport, although height is a disadvantage as anyone over 6'4" may have difficulty getting into a regular cockpit. There is little activity more peaceful than this once you are amid the clouds, and the best news is the danger levels are low. By far the biggest risk you face is colliding with another plane (extremely rare) and injuries in this sport are incurred at a lower rate than rugby.

SKYDIVING

Fancy hurling yourself out of a plane from a height of 13,500 feet and tumbling towards the ground at immense speed? Welcome to the hair-raising world of skydiving. Beginners start with a tandem skydive in which they are attached to the front of an instructor wearing a parachute. Generally, the instructor will control the first 30-45 second 'free-fall' element of the drop, open the parachute at around 5,000 feet, and then steer the parachute safely back to the landing area for a soft controlled landing. Air acrobatics (performed by your instructor) are often part and parcel of a descent.

Photograph by Ben Dawson of gliderpilot.co.uk

The activity is not cheap. Expect to pay around £200 if you attend a one-to-one session, less if you skydive as a group. Usually, prices include mandatory membership of the British Parachute Association and third party insurance cover for £2,000,000. There is a 15 stone (men) and 12 stone 7 pounds (women) maximum weight for tandem dives, and the sport is highly dependent on weather conditions – jumps only take place in clear conditions with winds of 20 knots (23 mph) or less. Anyone over the age of 16 can try it, although those over 40 will need to complete a medical form beforehand. Equipment is provided by the organisation or club where you perform the skydive (the British Parachute Association lists the UK's 'drop zones' and also charity dive opportunites), and all you will need are warm clothes, gloves and a hat.

If you enjoy the experience, there is the option of learning to skydive on your own and two-day courses are available if you wish to apply for a skydiving licence. Tandem dives are not much of a physical challenge (the instructor does most of the hard work including absorbing the impact when you land), but if you do progress to solo dives, it's a different matter. Prepare for adrenaline overload.

Photograph by Lorraine Dixcey, courtesy of skydivemag.com

WILD GYM DIRECTORY

Image courtesy of the Countryside Alliance

OUTDOOR EXERCISE CAMPAIGNING GROUPS

Many of these organisations run campaigns encouraging people to make the most of what the great outdoors has to offer.

countryside-alliance.org – The Alliance works for everyone who loves the countryside and the rural way of life, campaigning, lobbying and educating the public and government on the preservation of rural living.
countrysiderecreation.org.uk – The Countryside Recreation Network covers the UK and Republic of Ireland. It provides information on all aspects of countryside exercise and activities.
ccpr.org.uk – Central Council for Physical Recreation (CCPR) acts as an umbrella for the representative bodies of many sports and activities. It regularly holds campaigns to boost outdoor activity.
sportengland.org – Sport England is the government agency that advises, invests in and promotes community sport in England. Its website provides information on sports clubs and venues throughout the country, as well as how you can get involved in promoting sport in your community.
sports-council-wales.org.uk – Information on sport in Wales.
sportscotland.org.uk – The national agency for sport in Scotland with information about clubs and facilities.
sportni.net – Sport Northern Ireland for details of clubs and facilities in Northern Ireland.
trymysport.co.uk – A comprehensive sports web-directory, in which governing bodies of most sports in the UK provide contact and background information for beginners.
baha.org.uk – The British Activity Holiday Association is a trade website that provides a wealth of useful information and links to sites that offer activity holidays around the UK.
aals.org.uk – The Adventure Activities Licensing Scheme lists details of approved outdoor activity centres that adhere to a strict code of safety standards.

WALKING/RAMBLING

whi.org.uk – Walking the Way to Health, a joint initiative between Natural England and the British Heart Foundation that supports over 400 local walking schemes. Includes details of the National Stepometer Programme.
walkthewalk.org – Walk the Walk is a charity raising funds and awareness for breast cancer causes. They specialise in power walking challenges across the UK.
nordicwalking.co.uk – Provides information on Nordic walking classes, technique, poles and instructors that adhere to the standards of the International Nordic Walking Association (INWA).
polezing.com – Polezing is a fusion of Nordic walking and Pilates that incorporates toning and strengthening exercises as you walk with your poles.
ramblers.org.uk – Website of the Ramblers' Association with details about walks, group events and news.
ldwa.org.uk – Long Distance Walkers' Association for hikes with company beginning at 18 miles.
isleofwightwalkingfestival.co.uk – information about the UK's biggest walking festival.

BUGGY WORKOUTS

buggyfit.co.uk – Provides reasonably priced buggy workout classes throughout the UK, usually lasting an hour and covering a three to five mile route with targeted muscle group exercises.

postnatalexercise.co.uk – The Guild of Post Natal Exercise Instructors, for details of qualified trainers some of whom teach stroller sessions independently.

babyrunner.com and kidsense.co.uk – Stockists of all terrain and sports pushchairs.

strollerstrides.com and strollerfit.com – Provide information on US based buggy workouts.

RUNNING

runtrackdir.com – A directory of the 600 plus all-weather running tracks in the UK.

ukathletics.net – For details of running clubs, coaching and events.

runnersworld.co.uk – For details of running and triathlon events as well as training advice.

fellrunner.org.uk – The organisation coordinating and promoting fell (or hill/mountain) running in the UK.

Britishorienteering.org.uk – The governing body for orienteering in the UK. Provides news, events, fixtures, history and rankings and information about the sport.

runlondon.com – A website set up by Nike to encourage Londoners to make the most of the best running routes around the capital.

posetech.com – For details of the Pose Method of running and courses in the UK.

RUNNING VACATIONS

trailplus.com – Trail, cross country and marathon running camps held in the Forest of Dean and organised by former international athletes for runners of all levels.

runcatherina.com – For information about Chi Running courses with Irish running legend Catherina McKiernan.

runningthehighlands.com – Running holidays and breaks, training weekends and improver courses for athletes of all speeds held in the Eastern Cairngorms and Royal Deeside. Includes the Balmoral Training Weekend.

therunninginn.com – Running holidays for all capabilities held on the South Downs Country Park in Sussex and overseen by experienced runners Fiona Bugler and Mike Ovens.

running-holidays.co.uk – Running holidays on the beautiful Isle of Mull in the Western Isles of Scotland organised by John Hilton, a multi-marathon veteran.

runinthesun.com – Trail and road-running holidays for more experienced runners in Spain's Costa Blanca run by qualified athletics coaches.

PARK CIRCUITS

britmilfit.com – British Military Fitness is the biggest military style fitness provider in the UK, providing training sessions in parks across the country led by former army PT instructors.

outdoor-extreme.com – Run by Optimal Life Fitness, this company offers outdoor circuits using kettlebells that can be tailored to suit your specific goals, as well as six-week intensive fitness courses.

IN-LINE SKATING/ICE SKATING

skatefresh.com – Skatefresh's founder, Asha Kirkby, is a leading skate instructor, and offers in-line skating classes to private individuals and groups in London and Brighton.
citiskate.co.uk – For information about in-line skating events in the UK and abroad.
lfns.co.uk – London Friday Night Skate information.
pari-roller.com – For information about the weekly skate around the streets of Paris.
Skatepatrol.co.uk – Details of free beginner classes in London.
iisa.org – International In-line skating Association.
snowandrock.com, katesskates.co.uk and **slickwillies.co.uk** – Stockists of inline skates and protective gear.
iceskating.org.uk – For outdoor rinks and details of ice-skating lessons.
enjoyengland.com and **raisingkids.co.uk** – For a list of seasonal outdoor ice-rinks that usually open in December.

SKATEBOARDING

ukskate.org.uk – Home of the UK Skateboarding Association with information about competitions, clubs and rules of the sport.
sk8uk.co.uk – A useful resource for skateboarders of all abilities including tips on technique and information about venues.

BOWLS

bowlsengland.com – The unified governing body for outdoor flat green bowling in England, whose website lists information about clubs and courts around the UK, with links to other sites.
englishwomensbowling.net – The English Women's Bowling Association, which is part of Bowls England.

CROQUET

croquet.org.uk – The Croquet Association (CA) provides details of tournament, garden and golf croquet in the UK.
tradgames.org.uk – For a history of croquet and other games.

FREE RUNNING/PARKOUR

urbanfreeflow.com – This is the world's largest parkour and free running organisation, and they have been instrumental in bringing the sport to the public eye. The website provides great tips, links and forums.
parkouruk.com – A network of free runners in the UK.

ULTIMATE

ukultimate.com – The UK Ultimate Association's website lists upcoming tournaments, area teams, practice details, pictures, a history of the sport and past results.
wfdf.org – The World Flying Disc Federation is the governing body of the sport, and provides information on rules and competitions.

RECUMBENT CYCLING

londonrecumbents.co.uk or **rainbow-recumbents.co.uk** – For details of where to hire and buy recumbent bikes.
whycycle.co.uk – An independent site with useful advice about buying and riding recumbents.

KORFBALL

Englandkorfball.co.uk, welshkorfball.org and **scotlandkorfball.co.uk** – The governing bodies for korfball in the UK. Their websites provide comprehensive information about clubs and leagues.
Korfball.com – Useful links to korfball sites.

TAI CHI

taichiunion.com – The British Union for all tai chi styles and information about clubs and teachers.
tcfe.org – The Taijiquan and Qigong Federation for Europe (TCFE), which brings together individual practitioners and organisations throughout Europe.
taichicaledonia.com – An annual, international week-long event at the Stirling University Campus providing varied tai chi instruction in beautiful surrounds.
taichido.com – A site run by Southampton University which provides useful resources about tai chi in the UK.
chirunning.com – The official site for Chi Running, as set up by Danny Dreyer. It provides information about Chi Running courses and workshops as well as tips, shopping and a noticeboard.

OUTDOOR SWIMMING

outdoorswimmingsociety.co.uk – For events, tips and general information.
environment-agency.gov.uk – The website of the leading public organisation for protecting and improving the environment in England and Wales. This is the place to check for weather and pollution conditions in lakes and rivers.
river-swimming.co.uk – For more information about safety when swimming in Britain's rivers.
swimtrek.com – Organised outdoor swim excursions in venues ranging from the Scottish Inner Hebrides and the Lake District to the Greek Cyclades and the River Thames.
artofswimming.com – For tuition in the Shaw Method of swimming in venues such as Tuscany, Florida and Sicily as well as the UK.

FISHING

nfadirect.com – The National Federation of Anglers, whose website lists clubs, membership details and environmental reports.
salmon-trout.org – The Salmon and Trout Association, founded in 1903, which includes details of learn-to-fish schemes and water information for England and Wales.
castingforrecovery.org.uk – Casting for Recovery is a charity that organises rehabilitation through fishing for sufferers of breast cancer.
elfa.org.uk – England Ladies Fly Fishing Association, providing details of women only fishing events around the UK.

CANOEING/KAYAKING

bcu.org.uk – British Canoe Union for approved schools and clubs.

nationalwatersportsevents.co.uk – National Watersports Centre at Holme Pierrepont in Nottingham where there is a manmade white water slalom course open daily.

SAILING

rya.org.uk – Royal Yachting Association for approved clubs and places to learn.

ROWING

ara-rowing.org – The Amateur Rowing Association for information about clubs and coaching in the UK.

HORSE RIDING

bhs.org.uk – The British Horse Society for details of approved clubs and schools in the UK.

bef.co.uk – British Equestrian Federation, the governing body for Olympic Equestrian sports in the UK.

americanequestrian.com/hippotherapy – Background information on hippotherapy.

BODY BOARDING

britsurf.co.uk – British Surfing Association for details of schools and clubs.

orcasurf.co.uk – Home of numerous surfing magazines and communities, as well as a substantial surfshop.

KITE FLYING

bkfa.org.uk – British Kite Flying Association, a relatively new governing body of the hobby of kite flying and the more extreme variants of the sport, kitesurfing and kiteboarding.

thekitesociety.org.uk – The Kite Society of Great Britain – a leading organisation with a quarterly publication listing upcoming events, festivals and other kite-related news.

kiteman.co.uk – An independent website run by self-proclaimed 'kiteman' Malcolm Goodman that contains heaps of useful information.

kitesurfer.org – The official site of the British Kitesurfing Association.

GARDENING

btcv.co.uk – British Trust for Conservation Volunteers, organisers of the Green Gym campaign which encourages group gardening for health benefits.

thrive.org.uk – The horticultural charity Thrive promotes the use of gardening for health.

OFF-ROAD RUNNING

ukathletics.net – For details of cross country clubs and races.

tra-uk.org – UK Trail Running Association to meet other like minded runners in your area.

trailrunning.co.uk – Useful site listing everything for the trail runner; events, forum, photos and results, as well as details of new and scenic trails for running around the UK.

lakelandtrails.org – Lakeland Trails organises inspiring races in beautiful locations for all ages and abilities.

TREE CLIMBING

goodleaf.co.uk – Recreational tree climbing in the Isle of Wight for all ages and abilities.
mighty-oak.co.uk – Tree climbing courses in Cornwall.
treeclimbing.com – Tree Climbers International for general information about the benefits of tree climbing.
treeclimbing.co.uk – School of Tree Climbing in Herefordshire where you can attend five-day residential courses.

LANDYACHTING

bsflyc.org.uk – British Federation of Sand and Land Yachting Clubs for information about coaching and lessons.
anglialandsailing.co.uk – Located near Royston, this long established land yachting club offers training and coaching as well as a two kilometre racing circuit.
Blokart.co.uk – For information about Blokarting lessons.

SLEDDOG RACING

sled-dogs.co.uk – The website of Cairngorm Sled Dog Centre in Aviemore.
sdas.org.uk – Sled Dog Association of Scotland, which aims to raise awareness of the sport UK-wide.
members.aol.com/absauk/absaweb.htm - Affiliated British Sleddog Activities has a pretty basic site, but is a good starting point to learn more about the sport.
webheads.co.uk/sleddog/main – The British Musher's Association has good links and background information.
cani-cross.co.uk – For details of canine cross country events around the UK and abroad.

GOLF

englishgolfunion.org and **scottishgolfunion.org** – The governing bodies of the men's game in England and Scotland respectively.
lgu.org – Ladies Golf Union for details of women-friendly clubs and competitions.
getintogolf.co.uk – Get Into Golf, a campaign to encourage juniors and adults to take up the game.
celtic-manor.com – The Celtic Manor is an exclusive hotel in Wales which is to stage the 2010 Ryder Cup. It holds instruction courses as well as Golf Doctor weekends in which you can learn how Pilates and postural awareness can benefit your game.

FALCONRY

britishfalconersclub.co.uk – The British Falconers Club is the oldest falconry organisation in the UK, with plenty of background information and details of where to try the sport.
gleneagles.com – For information about falconry breaks with the British School of Falconry at the world famous Gleneagles Hotel in Scotland.

MOUNTAIN BOARDING / ROLLERSKI

atb-wales.co.uk – The home of all terrain boarding in Wales.
londonbeachstore.co.uk – A fantastic shop in the heart of the West End where you can buy or hire all terrain boards and book lessons.
outtograss.com – A mountainboarding centre in Herefordshire that provides facilities for both experienced boarders and beginners.
mountainboarding.co.uk – A dedicated mountainboarding centre in Halifax.
rollerski.co.uk – For details of the sport and lessons available in the South East of England.
londonnordic.org.uk – Training and events for rollerskiing and cross country skiing for both amateurs and serious racers.

ADVENTURE RACING

dynamicadventure racing.co.uk, aceraces.co.uk and **questars.co.uk** – These companies all organise adventure races in the UK and hold details of those held abroad. They also offer coaching clinics and training camps.
extremeiironing.com – home of the adventure sport of extreme (under the sky) ironing.

STREET LUGING

streetluge.co.uk – For details of where to try it, where to get a board and how to meet up with other street lugers. They also stage street luge taster days for beginners.
gofastsports.co.uk – Energy drinks company Go Fast! sponsors extreme sports including downhill mountain biking, base jumping and street luging, organising events and sponsoring athletes.
auldovertheroad.com – the website of X-Games medalist Dave Auld, providing a personal account of streetluging, as well as comprehensive links and a noticeboard.

ZORBING

adrenalinemunky.com – A Surrey based zorbing park that is run association with international zorbing company Downhill Revolution.
zorbsouth.co.uk – A zorbing centre in Dorset with a very fast 200 metre zorb run.
zorb.com – Background details of zorbing.

SKIING AND SNOWBOARDING

skiclub.co.uk – The Ski Club of Great Britain provides a comprehensive site with advice on all aspects of snowsports and planning holidays. It is worth joining this club simply to get the benefits of their well-organised package holidays with top instructors as well as receiving a free magazine.
snowsportgb.com – The British Ski and Snowboard Federation is the governing body of snowsports in the UK and the organisation that represents racing and international competition.
ski.visitscotland.com – For information about ski resorts in Scotland.

MOUNTAIN BIKING

ctc.org.uk – The Cyclists' Touring Club is the UK's largest national cycling membership organization, protecting and promoting the rights of cyclists since 1878. Its website provides a wealth of information about getting started on bikes of any description.
sustrans.org.uk – Sustrans is the UK's leading sustainable transport charity and provides details of the 10,000 miles of national cycle paths in the UK.
mbr.co.uk – For mountain bike routes in the UK.
britishcycling.org.uk – The British Cycling Federation which is the governing body of competitive domestic and international cycling. It provides information about mountain bike races and competitions as well as cycling clubs.

ORIENTEERING

britishorienteering.org.uk – Orienteering is represented nationally by the British Orienteering Federation based in Bath.

FELL RUNNING

fellrunner.org.uk – The Fell Running Association for information about races and clubs.

CLIMBING

thebmc.co.uk – The British Mountaineering Council site has a complete directory of climbing clubs and venues in the UK.
climber.co.uk – Climber magazine is packed with tips and features climbing routes from around the world.
ukclimbing.com – Has an overview of UK climbing grades and a database of 3,500 climbing routes across the UK and the world.
mountaingirl.eu – For details about women-only climbing courses in Europe.
pyb.co.uk – The national mountain centre based in Wales, Plas y Brenin is a registered charity that offers training in a range of mountain sports including climbing, skiing, kayaking and hillwalking.

CROSS COUNTRY SKIING

escnordic.org.uk – English Ski Council Nordic Committee for general information about the sport.
crosscountryski.co.uk – Books, links and background information about the sport.
activity-scotland.org.uk – For cross country skiing tuition and holidays in Scotland.
nordicski.co.uk – Huntly Nordic Ski Club with details of the own of the Clashindarroch forest with forest trails designated for cross country skiing and mountain biking.

GORGE WALKING

blackmountain.co.uk – Adventure holidays in Wales including gorge walking, white water rafting, kayaking, abseiling, mountain biking and many more.
iain.co.uk – Gorge walking and bog trotting in the Peak district.
adventureswales.co.uk – For details of gorge walking and other activity holidays in Wales.
climb365.net – Gorge walking, climbing and mountaineering in the Lake District.

POTHOLING

british-caving.org.uk – British Caving Association, the governing body of caving in the UK.
cavinguk.com – Information about caving clubs, venues and regular weather forecasts.

DINGHY SAILING

Dinghysailingmagazine.co.uk – The only magazine exclusively about dinghy sailing. It's a monthly publication detailing tips, techniques and insights into the sport.
hovelagoon.co.uk – Learn to sail with Lagoon Watersports in Sussex.

BALLOONING

high-adventure.co.uk – Hot air ballooning in the Lake District.
goballooning.co.uk – Offers UK-wide balloon rides and pilot taster sessions for adults.

WHITEWATER RAFTING

ukrafting.co.uk – Canolfan Tryweryn is the National Whitewater Centre based in north Wales. It was the first commercial whitewater rafting operation in the UK in 1986, has since grown to become the largest and most well-respected rafting organisation in the UK.
nenewhitewatercentre.co.uk – Whitewater rafting, kayaking and canoeing courses from March to November in Northamptonshire.

CAMPING

featherdownfarms.co.uk – Feather Down Farms in the Midlands or South West of England offer camping for urban softies. Your 'tent' is pre-erected, and has wooden floors and a stove but no hot water or electricity.
coolcamping.co.uk – An excellent site by travel writer Jonathan Knight with details of the coolest places to camp in England.
thehappycampers.co.uk – Campsites recommended by the authors of 'The Happy Campers' book, Tess Carr and Cat Heyes.
yha.org.uk – For details of the Youth Hostel Association's 40 'camping barns' run by farmers in stunning rural locations. Offering little more than a roof over your head, they generally offer just sleeping platforms, areas to eat and prepare food, and cold running water.
larkhilltipis.co.uk – At Larkhill Farm in Carmarthenshire, Wales, you can sleep in a Tipi or Mongolian-style Yurt, a wooden, canvas-covered structure with floorboards, a calor gas stove and futons inside and situated in four acres of woodland.
larosa.co.uk – La Rosa gypsy caravans near Whitby has caravans in a woodland setting with a circus-style marquee as a central meeting point for night time get-togethers around steaming cauldrons on an open fire pit.

CONSERVATION VACATIONS

nationaltrust.org.uk – With the National Trust, the largest organiser of conservation schemes, you can opt to carry out repairs to the ice-sculpted footpaths of the Brecon Beacons, dry stonewalling in Yorkshire or Scotland or building a Mongolian Yurt in Snowdownia. If you are put off by the idea of a week's hard graft and no play, they also offer a programme that combines a few days conservation activities with two days of cycling or hiking in the surrounding countryside.

jmt.org – The John Muir Trust owns and manages protected land in the highlands and islands of Scotland and offers conservation projects for members.

ADVENTURE FITNESS

wildfitness.com – Get back to nature and get fit at the same time in a beautiful coastal region of Kenya.

BUSHCRAFT AND SURVIVAL COURSES

backwoodssurvival.co.uk – Patrick McGlinchey, the founder of Backwoods Survival School, spent long periods travelling remote corners of the globe armed with only his clothing, a knife and metal cup. The skills he picked up along the way are at the heart of these tough courses in the highlands of Scotland.

primitiveways.com – A website with useful resources and also details of survival courses in the USA.

raymears.com – Ray Mears, the UK's best known presenter and author on survival and bushcraft skills, is also the owner of the Woodlore school of Wilderness Bushcraft. It offers a range of different survival experiences including family weekends and four-day courses for unaccompanied 11 to 16-year-olds.

uksurvivalschool.co.uk – The UK Survival School offers a comprehensive programme of wilderness skills courses in the Brecon Beacons, Herefordshire and the Isle of Skye. They also offer arctic, mountain, jungle and desert wilderness skills courses in locations throughout the world including Norway, Borneo, Oman, Australia and Namibia, learning the skills first hand from the Indigenous peoples of the regions.

cambriansurvival.co.uk – Learn survival skills in the rugged Cambrian Mountains of Wales.

survival-school.org – Trueways Survival Schools, around the UK, offer a gentle introduction to the scene including one-day navigation and signalling courses.

natural-pathways.co.uk – Holds family survival courses for ages six and upwards.

NAVIGATION SKILLS

nnas.org.uk – The National Navigation Award Scheme.

www.snowdonia-adventures.co.uk – Snowdonia Adventures specialise in providing skills courses for walkers, climbers and mountaineers including navigation courses, coasteering and rock climbing.

WOODLAND LIVING

rivercottage.net – Chef Hugh Fearnley-Whittingstall and his team hold courses in getting the most out of wild food with courses such as 'mushroom foraging', 'herbal hedgerows', and 'edible seashore'.

natural-pathways.co.uk – For courses in flint-napping and other woodland skills.

tamarackbushcraft.co.uk – For wilderness cookery courses.

NIGHT CYCLING

fattirebiketoursparis.com – For details of organised night bike rides through Paris from February to November.
snowdoniacyclehire.co.uk – Night biking courses in north Wales.
forestfreeride.co.uk – Offer mountain bike skills courses, tuition and guiding for all levels, including two-hour off-road night cycling tours in forests of Wales.
midnightridazz.com – For details of monthly night cycling events in Los Angeles.
nycgov.parks.org – Information about the monthly Central Park Moonlight Rides.

COASTEERING

britishcoasteeringfederation.co.uk – An organisation formed in 2006 to introduce safety guidelines and measures for this activity.
tyf.com – TYF is widely seen as 'the home' of coasteering, having pioneered the development of the activity from 1986 onwards. They also offer courses in sea kayaking, surfing and rock climbing.
activitywales.com – For details of coasteering on the Pembrokeshire coast.

RAP RUNNING AND FREEFALL ABSEILING

naelimits.co.uk – Try rap running and freefall abseiling on a 150 foot high cliff with a natural overhang in Scotland.
ultimatelimits.co.uk – Rap running and freefall abseiling in Perthshire.

GLIDING

gliding.co.uk – British Gliding Association for details about clubs and courses.
gliderpilot.co.uk – A useful website with links, stories, information about learning to fly and tips for pilots.
bookergliding.co.uk – Gliding courses and tuition at the Booker gliding Club near High Wycombe in Buckinghamshire.

SKYDIVING

bpa.org.uk – British Parachute Association for details of courses and events around the country.
ukskydiving.com – Lessons at the North London parachute centre.

SOURCES

INTRODUCTION

...inhabitants of the Industrialised West spend 93 per cent of their time inside: University of Michigan news service, October 2004

...Britons work the longest hours in Europe: Trades Union Congress, 2006

...many parents deny their children the chance to enjoy the freedom they had: The Children's Society's Good Childhood report, 2007

...today's children are more likely to suffer injuries brought on by playing computer games: Royal Society for the Prevention of Accidents report at Play Safety Conference, 2007

...in 1995, 68 per cent of children ages seven to 11 rode a bike at least six times a year: reports by the National Sporting Goods Association and American Sports Data, 2005

When a group of 64 volunteers... The Journal of Aging and Health, February 2006

Aerobic activity, in particular, has been shown to prevent age-related mental decline: study at University of Illinois at Urbana in Champaign presented at the 114th annual convention of the American Psychological Association (APA), 2006

One in four GP consultations is for depression: National Health Service 2005
Research from Japan and the Netherlands has shown that just living close to a green space means people live longer and enjoy better health: Tanaka A, Takano T, Nakamura K, et al. Health Levels Influenced by Urban Residential Conditions in a Megacity—Tokyo. Urban Study, 1996; Healthy places: exploring the evidence, Am J Public Health, 2003

Surveys by the fitness industry show that most people throw in the towel six months after forking out a hefty gym subscription: Healthclub Benchmark Report, 2006

Three quarters of gym members even schedule their gym visits to coincide with a specific television programme: Leisure Connection Survey, 2005

Researchers found that many gym members become so engrossed in a TV show: Study at Cooper Aerobic Centre, Dallas, 2005

...a teaspoon of whirlpool tub water had an average of 2.17m bugs in one American study: Texas A&M University, 2006

One survey tested water from eight pools in the London area and found levels of chemical by-products, called trihalomethanes [corr], were much higher in pool water than in tap water: Journal Occupational and Environmental Medicine, 2005

Saunas have been found to contain high levels of cirobacter freundii: Survey by University College Hospital for Men's Fitness magazine, 2006

Researchers found high amounts of staphylococcus epidermis, which causes skin infections, on the bench-press headrest and dumbbells in UK gyms: Survey by University College Hospital for Men's Fitness magazine 2006

Official crime figures show that attacks on women outside the home are relatively infrequent: British Crime Survey

...the most damaging for outdoor exercisers is a high ozone level which is more usually found in rural areas: Friends of the Earth, 2006

Researchers found that levels of the chemical phenylethylamine, similar in structure to amphetamines, increase substantially during exercise: Phenylethylamine, A Possible Link to the Antidepressant Effects of Exercise? Szabo, Billet and Turner, Br J Sports Med, 2001

WILD GYM IN THE CITY

...researchers found that urbanites are more likely to be active: Survey by Statistics Canada, 2006

Research has shown that people who live in built up areas tend to walk further: Survey by Statistics Canada, 2006

Studies have shown that using poles forces people to walk faster: Study at University of Wisconsin, 1997

Studies have shown that regular running could reduce the risk of heart disease: Study by Harvard School of Public health, JAMA, 2002

Researchers looked at the strength and endurance of leg muscles as well as flexibility in the knee, ankle and hip joints: Study at the Chinese University of Hong Kong, British Journal Sports Medicine, 2006

A study of 78 year-olds prone to falling significantly improved their strength, balance and stability with a 12-week course of Tai Chi: Journal of Advanced Nursing, June 2005

A review of 47 studies looking at the impact Tai Chi had on people with chronic health problems like heart disease or multiple sclerosis: Archives of Internal Medicine, April 2004

One study found that regular classes gave patients who had suffered heart failure better movement: American Journal of Medicine, November 2004

Australian Researchers found that, among women diagnosed with post-natal depression, those who completed a 12-week stroller class showed fewer symptoms: International Journal of Nursing Practice, 2004

WILD GYM IN THE WATER

Rivers and lakes in the UK are cleaner than they have been for 150 years - about 75 per cent are safe to swim in: Environment Agency

Studies in the UK and America show that 67 per cent of people who can swim are afraid of deep water: Boston Globe, May 8, 2006

American research has shown that waist-deep water reduces the pressures on joints by 50 per cent: American College of Sports Medicine

A study carried out on male rowers, triathletes and sedentary controls found that rowers had significantly higher bone mass density (BMD) in the spine, an area traditionally vulnerable to osteoporosis: European Journal of Applied Physiology, volume 97, May 2006

Another study on 14 female rowers and showed that not only did the rowers have higher BMD in the lumbar spine, but also that during a 6-minute race, the muscular pull forces generated in the spine were equivalent to 4.6 times body weight, a figure that compares favourably with that attained during weight training, which is widely considered as one of the very best bone building exercises: Indoor Rowing for Bone Health, Concept II, 2006

Studies have shown that after 12 weeks of training, top level canoeists had very low levels of body fat: Australian Institute of Sport

Researchers found that the average mass of the heart's left chamber was 50 per cent greater in canoeists than in non-exercisers: American Heart Association, 2005

A Turkish study of 60 men ages 15 to 21 showed that sand running produced a greater increase in calf circumference over road running: The Journal of Strength and Conditioning Research: Vol. 12, 1998

A Belgian study concluded that walking on dry sand requires 2.1 to 2.7 times more energy than does walking on a hard surface at the same speed: European Journal of Applied Physiology, volume 65, 1992

A study by Japanese and Australian researchers compared the impact effects of jumping onto sand versus wooden gym floors, concluding that training on sand may carry a lower risk of impact injury than working out on harder surfaces: Washington Post, June 7 2005

Australian physiotherapists were among the first in the scientific world to shed light on the fact that many people would be better off working out with no trainers than spending a small fortune on the latest high tech shoes: Sportscience 5 (3), December 2001

WILD GYM IN THE COUNTRYSIDE

...each year some 1.5 billion day visits are made to the UK's rural areas: Countryside Alliance, 2007

A study of hikers in the Alps found that different types of walking had different effects on fats and sugars in the blood: American Heart Association Scientific Sessions, November 2004

Just three long walks a week can reduce waist and hip circumference and lower blood pressure: Preventative Medicine 44 (2), February 2007

Other researchers looked at the effects of walking on stony ground: Journal of the American Geriatrics Society, July 2005

One study found backward training improved cardiorespiratory fitness while helping to streamline the physique of a group of novice runners: International Journal Sports Medicine (26), 2005

Studies comparing road running to running on rough terrains: British Journal of Sports Medicine (32), 1998

One American study showed falls account for 45 per cent of riding injuries: Injuries in horseback riding: a review; Sports Medicine (9), 1990

WILD GYM IN THE MOUNTAINS

Scandinavian research reports a high rate of lower back pain among high level cross-country skiers with some studies showing up to two thirds of racers experience it at some time: Oslo Sports Trauma Research Centre study, 2004

Too many hours on a bicycle saddle have been shown to compress the artery and vital nerves leading to the penis, increasing the risk of numbness, pain, and erectile dysfunction: MedicineNet, 2007

Research has found that ageing orienteers, compared with non-athletes, had faster reaction speeds and better attention skills: American Association for Leisure and Recreation, 2001

Studies have shown that fell runners have much higher concentrations of aerobic enzymes - the chemicals which allow your muscles to function at high intensity for long periods without fatigue - in their quadriceps muscles at the front of the thigh than those who did all their running on flat terrain: Institute of Sports Science Copenhagen, 2006

Researchers have found that running uphill gives you a cardiovascular workout and lowers triglycerides (blood fats) that are a risk factor for heart disease: Study at Academic Teaching Hospital Feldkirch, Austria presented at American Heart Association Scientific Sessions, 2004

ACKNOWLEDGEMENTS

So many organisations and individuals showed incredible generosity and enthusiasm when we approached them about this book, helping us out with research, insights and imagery, without which the book would not have been possible.

Thanks first and foremost to the various charities, sports governing bodies and other organisations who have provided invaluable technical tips and insider knowledge for their respective activities.

Many thanks to Jill Grieve at the Countryside Alliance and to John Ainsworth at Sport England for their contribution of numerous images. Thanks also to Amanda Boorman at LaRosa, Steve Borrill at Anglia Landyachting Club, Asha Kirkby at Skatefresh, Barney Larkin at British Military Fitness, Carl Durham at Black Mountain, Caroline Povey at British Orienteering, Danny Dreyer of Chi Running, EZ at Urban Freeflow, Tony James at the British Falconers Club, Stuart at Forest Freeride, Gary Jack at Bowls England, Ben Dawson of Glider Pilot, Paul McCathie from Goodleaf Tree Climbing, Graham Patten from Trailrunning, Justin from Adrenaline Munky, Kris Yule at Go Fast! Francis Mitchell at Nordic Walking UK, Paul Magner at Trailplus, Dave Cheetham of Plas y Brenin, Susannah Field at River Cottage HQ, Mark Handford of Snowdonia Adventures, Maggie Lawrie at Snowsport GB, Emma Redding of Buggyfit, Tommy Matthews at Optimal Life Fitness, Steven Shaw at Art of Swimming, Luke Rowlands from the TYF group, Ged Lawless at UK Survival School and Tom Williams at WHI.

We are also indebted to the individual photographers who contributed to the book – Alistair Brown, Britta Sendlhofer, Dave Auld, Dr Matthew Gage, Katie Ellis, Michael Smith, Ronnie Robinson, Peter Koyander, Dom Taylor and Zillah Crosby, as well as all the Guardian staff photographers whose images were used.

Finally, thanks to Lisa Darnell, Ziggy Hanaor and Kevan Westbury for pulling everything together so brilliantly.